Raising Healthy Birds

*Good health and nutrition advice
for your new pet bird.*

The Editors of Bird Talk and
Bird Breeder Magazines

BOWTIE PRESS

Mission Viejo, California

Raising Healthy Birds
Good Health and Nutrition Advice for Your New Pet Bird.

Kathleen Etchepare
and the Editors of Bird Talk and Bird Breeder magazines

Created, edited and produced by Bowtie Press
Editor in Chief: Gene Booth
Design: Dirk Hagner
Art Direction: Jeff Dombrowski
Illustrations: Chas. Balun

First Edition

Library of Congress Cataloging-in-Publications Data
Etchepare, Kathleen
Raising healthy birds /by Kathleen Etchepare and the editors
of Bird Talk and Bird Breeder magazines

Bibliography: p.
Includes Index.
ISBN 0-9629525-4-0 (pbk.) $12.95
1. Animals.........

Library of Congress Catalog Card Number LC 95-79490

Printed in the United States of America by Banta Press
First printing 1995   9 8 7 6 5 4 3 2 1

Bowtie Press
Fancy Publications, Inc.
Post Office Box 6050
Mission Viejo CA 92690-0050

Contents

THE PHYSICAL FEATURES OF BIRDS

APPENDICES

Foreword

Being a Good 'Parent'

By Kathleen Etchepare

*Imagine this: You have no job; no money; no health insurance; no ability to pre-
pare your own food, bathe yourself, clean your room (which is also your bathroom) or
get yourself to a doctor should you become ill; you do not speak the same language as
those who would be able to help you; and you cannot build items for your amusement
or entertainment. If you didn't have a very compassionate caretaker who understood
and fulfilled your personal needs, you would be in big trouble.*

*Now, think about your pet bird. How closely do you monitor its diet? Do you con-
sider the fact that birds live much longer, happier, healthier lives when fed a nutritionally balanced diet? Do you keep a sharp eye for any subtle changes or symptoms of illness? Once a bird begins to show obvious signs of illness (sitting on the bottom of the
cage, listlessness, loss of appetite, loose droppings and so on), it is probably close to death.
Do you spend adequate time with your bird and offer it the attention it needs so badly
to remain in good emotional health?*

*You may be thinking, "I don't need this guilt trip." Remember, though, exotic
birds are highly intelligent creatures. They require a lot of attention and items with
which to amuse themselves when their owners are away from home. Exotic pet birds are
not domesticated animals like dogs and horses. They retain all the instincts of their
cousins in the wild. One of those, unfortunately for them, is the survival instinct—
which dictates that they conceal symptoms of illness. In the wild, this protects sick birds
from becoming easy prey for enemies. In captivity, this means that by the time many
owners recognize signs of illness, it is often too late for even the most talented avian veterinarian to save the bird's life.*

*The only way that we as pet bird owners can be "good parents" to our special
feathered charges is to educate ourselves on such subjects as proper avian nutrition and
preventive avian health care. Providing some of that knowledge is the goal of this bird
health book.*

*While reading the chapters, you may find that some veterinarians, behaviorists or
nutritionists have their own opinions on various facets of subjects. All, you will discover, are valid and will help you better understand your particular bird's needs. Every
bird is an individual, and if you are a caring owner, you understand your pet better
than anyone else in the world. Educate yourself; devour all the information you can;
and then use the information you believe best applies to your pet.*

*Not everyone can be a good pet bird "parent," but by making the commitment to
learn more about your bird's needs, you are taking the first step toward that goal.*

The average parrot has 350 taste buds. Despite this seemingly low number of taste buds, many parrots have well-developed ideas of what tastes good to them.

Birds' Dietary Needs

Dale R. Thompson

For many people, pet birds are an integral part of the family unit, and it is up to conscientious owners to fill their pets' emotional and physical needs. One of the most important ways we can contribute to our birds' long, healthy lives is to offer them a nutritionally balanced diet.

In the wild, all birds spend considerable time foraging for food — an activity that provides exercise as well as a varied diet. This diversity allows wild birds to receive the many components found in a nutritionally balanced diet. Not only do they have a medley of food items to choose from, but the types of food also change throughout the year depending upon the season. Birds will follow the fruiting plants and trees as they become ripe.

In captivity, pet birds depend on their owners to supply them with a nutritionally balanced diet. In the past, dry seed diets were primarily used because they are easy to feed and readily accepted by birds; however, we now know that dry seed-only diets are nutritionally inadequate for pet birds. This does not mean that dry seeds are bad for pet birds, but dry seeds should be given in reduced amounts supplemented with a selection of other food items.

Nutritionally deficient diets can make birds more susceptible to diseases, infections and many physical ailments. Feather-chewing, skin and eye problems, poor feather structure and sheen, and some other physical maladies often can be attributed to poor nutrition.

BALANCING THE DIET

Because the needs of various pet birds are quite different, no single solution exists to supplying them a nutritious diet. Some

The Four Food Groups
Offering your birds a seed-only diet is not offering them a balanced diet. Remember the four basic food groups. Besides seed, which satisfies the grain group, birds should receive protein in the form of legumes, split peas and hard-boiled eggs; fresh fruits and vegetables; and some calcium, preferably in the form of supplements.

Cut fruits and vegetables into small pieces so your bird can carry them to a perch to eat.

birds are wild-caught, while others were hand-fed as babies. Certain birds are very picky in their food habits, and others are wasteful. The consistency of food and needs of various species also differ: Lories need high-energy, moistened food or nectar; budgies and cockatiels eat more dry foods; and many large parrots, such as macaws and Amazons, consume an abundance of fruit.

If we can supply our birds with foods that belong to the four major food groups needed for survival, they will live out their lives in good health. These four food groups include: grains, fruits and vegetables, protein sources, and sources of calcium (known as the dairy group for human beings).

Grains: The grain group supplies many vitamins, minerals and proteins. Grains provide energy from simple and complex carbohydrates. Seeds fall within this group, but since many pet birds prefer dry seeds over almost all other foods, seeds must be limited. Millet seeds come in a variety of sizes and colors. Canary seed is high in protein, while oat groats and sunflower are high in fat.

Other good grain sources include wheat (red winter wheat), rice (brown or paddy), oats, barley and sorghum. Many grains and seeds can be germinated by soaking them for 12 to 24 hours and then allowing them to sprout throughout the next 24 to 72 hours. This method can promote the development of mold, however, so extreme

care should be taken to avoid spoilage. To prevent this, add a mold inhibitor like calcium propionate to the water during the soak period and frequently rinse the seeds during the germinating period. Human types of food within the grain group include whole-wheat or stone-ground bread and pasta. Although our pet birds always appreciate the grain group, it lacks many of the essential nutrients found in the other food groups.

Fruits and vegetables: This food group is certainly important for our birds' health. It supplies many important vitamins including vitamin A, many of the B vitamins, vitamin E and vitamin K. Vitamin A is important for growth, and for the absorption of calcium and vitamin D; it is also necessary for the prevention of infection and the development of good skin lining. Many vegetables contain vitamin A, but those with an especially high content include carrots, yams, winter squash, broccoli and dark green vegetables like chard or New Zealand spinach.

Fruits with vitamin A include papayas, cantaloupe and apricots. Some fleshy fruits, such as apples, bananas and celery, have a high water content and are low in many nutrients, but I use them as an emotional "comfort food" for my birds. I believe they are an "elixir of life" for them. The B vitamins that are so important for the health of our pet birds are found in alfalfa, soybeans, beets and again in the dark leafy vegetables.

Leafy vegetables should be fed fresh and removed immediately if they show any signs of wilting or spoilage. Pet birds relish garden vegetables, including green beans and peas, all the legumes, and fresh carrot or beet tops. The pods of many of these vegetables can satisfy the birds' natural need to peel foods. However, make sure to cut large fruits and vegetables into small pieces so that your bird can pick up and carry the food to its perch to eat it if it so desires, and to ensure that discarded food drops through cage grating and out of reach of curious beaks.

Vitamin C is crucial during times of stress or illness. Once a week I give a slice of citrus fruit to my birds, and they always relish it. Frozen single or mixed vegetables are convenient for owners of single pet birds. A portion can be broken off and thawed, leaving the rest in the freezer — making for little waste.

Protein group: This food group always includes meat, but since meat is seldom fed to pet birds, plant proteins are better suited to their needs. The most popular animal protein consumed by birds is eggs. Cooked eggs (boiled for more than 20 minutes to eliminate possible *Salmonella*) are used in many egg food recipes for baby canaries, finches and even some parakeets.

Plant proteins are found in legumes, the most common being in the bean group. Commonly fed beans include navy, kidney, garbanzo and soybeans. Most are soaked overnight and cooked (to a boil) in the morning. Often a crock pot is used to slow cook these very hard food items. Overcooking should be avoided as it will destroy many of the vitamins. Other protein sources include green split peas and lentils, which supply many of the amino acids not found in the grains.

Products that supply calcium: This group includes many products not fed to birds. For humans this group provides amino acids, vitamins and calcium. For birds, these nutrients can be found in the other food groups or can be offered in the form of vitamin supplements. The main dairy food consumed by humans is milk, but because birds have great difficulty digesting the sugars in milk, it should not be fed to them. Cheese, however, can be offered in very small pieces, infrequently, as a treat.

SUPPLEMENTS

Water-soluble vitamins lose their potency after three to four hours; they can also

Pet birds relish garden vegetables, including beet tops. Feed beet and carrot tops fresh to your bird, and remove the tops immediately if they show signs of wilting or spoilage.

be the media for bacteria growth in the water dish. Powdered vitamins sprinkled on soft foods are more effective. A multivitamin high in vitamin A made especially for birds is excellent. Dicalcium phosphate and trace minerals can also be sprinkled on the food. Small amounts placed consistently on the food are better than large amounts because many birds will avoid foods with a gritty texture.

PELLETED DIETS

Most of the research on the nutritional needs of exotic birds has come from nutritional research in the poultry industry, so it is not surprising that commercial diets have now been produced for parrots and other nondomestic birds. Originally, poultry products, such as turkey or game bird crumble, were used for exotic birds; these were followed by the use of commercial dog kibble.

Now an abundance of commercial exotic bird formulated diets is available for just about every species found in captivity. These diets were formulated to overcome the nutritional deficiencies found in seed-only diets. These products come in two forms: pellets and extruded formulas. The difference between the two is this: Ground or mashed food ingredients in pellets are heated under great pressure to form a hard pellet. Extruded diets also put the mashed food ingredients under heated pressure, but air is forced through tiny holes to create a fluffy pellet not unlike our human breakfast cereals. Minute air pockets have been trapped within the extruded formula-type pellet, creating a lighter product.

Such a large variety of these diets are available that I suggest owners interested in offering their birds a pelleted or extruded formula diet contact bird owners or breeders who have used a certain type successfully over a long period of time for advice. I personally take advantage of these commercial bird products, and they certainly have improved the overall nutrition of my birds. They provide a great nutritional base with vitamins and other supplements already added.

THE PERFECT DIET

As of yet, no long-term study on the nutrition of exotic birds in their natural habitat has been revealed. Obviously, though, exotic birds in the wild do not have the same dietary habits, let alone the same foods available, as exotic birds in captivity. The truth is, pet birds will not eat a nutritionally balanced diet even if we place a variety of food items in front of them. They will eat the food they like best, and if that item is strictly sunflower seed, they certainly will not have a balanced diet. One of the early problems with feeding commercial pelleted diets is that many birds do not recognize pellets as being a food item. Owners sometimes have to force their birds to accept pellets by removing some of their birds' favorite foods.

One of the best ways to get birds to accept different foods is to feed twice a day. Feed any new foods (pelleted diets or any unfamiliar foods) in the morning, and feed the familiar or favorite foods in the evening. The evening feeding can also be a time for sharing your dinner with your pet. The secret to gaining better acceptance of new foods is to limit the total amount of food at the evening feeding so your pet bird will be very hungry in the morning. It will then be more apt to try new foods. It may take some time and patience to go through the early trial period, but doing so will benefit your pet with a more nutritious diet.

Feeding twice a day also follows the natural times that birds in the wild eat. They generally fill their crops (a natural food storage chamber) in the early morning and again just before dusk. Because of the great diversity of birds and their habits, I do not believe that any one perfect diet exists. Getting your pet bird to accept a variety of foods will certainly benefit it nutritionally.

The diet I use includes one or more kinds of cooked beans (I especially recommend soybeans), cooked rice, a variety of both cooked and fresh vegetables (including corn, peas, green beans, green leafy vegetables, raw carrots and alfalfa sprouts). I feed nuts only as a treat.

There is nothing wrong with dry seeds, but they should be fed in limited amounts. I recommend canary seed, millet, wheat and/or sunflower. Seeds are best given in the evening feeding. Birds enjoy fruit immensely, but because of its limited nutritional value, no more than 10 percent of the total diet should consist of fruit. Getting your pet bird to accept one of the commercial avian pellets or extruded formulas is highly recommended, because they satisfy many nutritional requirements that may be lacking without them.

You can always change the types of foods offered with the seasons to give your pet some variety. Some say that human table food is inappropriate for pet birds. I believe it is all right if offered in very small amounts or as occasional treats.

We may be the owners of our pet birds, but these pets are also our friends and family members. The emotional satisfaction should be mutual between bird and human, and one way we can enjoy an ongoing relationship with our avian pets for many years is to supply them with a nutritionally balanced diet.

Seeds and Seed Mixes

Elaine Radford

A fresh, clean seed is a small miracle: a compact container that holds all the ingredients required to sprout a new plant. Depending on the type of seed and the area in which it is grown, seeds can offer a rich supply of nutrients for many kinds of pet birds. Seed is the traditional backbone of the pet bird's diet — to such a degree that some people still think birds can live on a diet of seed alone. Millet, for example, contains approximately 60 percent carbohydrates, the complex sugars and starches that provide quick energy for active, warm-blooded birds like finches. Sunflower seed, an oily seed, is about 55 percent fat, which, among other functions, keeps skin soft and feathers shiny.

DAYS OF OLD

Twenty or 30 years ago, few people would have guessed that seed would develop the "seedy" reputation it has in the last decade. When most breeders and hobbyists concentrated on raising zebra finches, budgerigars and cockatiels, the deficiencies of the 90- or 100-percent seed diets were not particularly obvious.

Zebras, budgies and cockatiels are tough little birds that come from the arid Australian grasslands. Their bodies seem designed to extract the last trace of nutrition from seeds and grains, allowing them to thrive and breed on diets that would slowly starve birds from richer environments. Although budgies sometimes developed iodine deficiencies if they didn't receive the proper supplements, most breeders probably didn't fully realize the importance of a varied diet until they began working with more challenging species.

Offer Seeds the Natural Way
Birds enjoy eating millet seeds in the form of dried seedling heads, called a millet spray. Eating from sprays is not only convenient for obvious reasons, but it also offers the birds some exercise by requiring them to work to remove the seeds from the spray.

CHANGING OPINION

Today, however, some people actually seem to be afraid of seed. Some breeders won't feed dry seed at all, condemning it as an unnecessary source of excess fat. Pet owners complain that their birds, particularly imported parrots that weren't exposed to varied diets early, appear to be hooked on seed. Breeders and pet owners alike worry that they're inadvertently harming their birds if they must rely on seed mixes to get enough calories into the diet.

Some of this concern is warranted. A pure seed diet will almost certainly shorten the life of your bird, just as a pure rice diet will almost certainly shorten the life of a human. But that doesn't mean seed and rice are bad or dangerous foods. Fed in appropriate amounts, seed remains one of the best sources of calories (energy) for many popular species of pet birds. By educating yourself about what your seed mix offers your bird, you can learn to provide a healthy, balanced diet that will help your pet thrive.

FAVORITE SMALL SEEDS

Seeds contain a varying mix of fats, proteins and carbohydrates, as well as trace nutrients like vitamins or minerals. Remember, a seed exists to produce a new baby plant, not to feed hungry birds. It contains such things as amino acids (the building blocks of protein) in a proportion designed to nourish a young sprout of its own species. These nutrients may be, and probably are, totally out of balance for a healthy bird. In the wild, bird flocks forage for many different types of ripening seeds at different times of the year. An amino acid missing from one seed is found in another food, providing a natural balance. Those of us raising birds in captivity must make sure our birds have a variety of seeds (and other foods) to supply this balance.

Millet, the backbone of most finch diets, is a low-fat, high-carbohydrate grain that provides a good source of quick energy to small, active birds. It's a good basic food commonly included in budgie, cockatiel and small hook-bill mixes as well as in finch mixes. In fact, I sometimes buy millet in health food stores for my own consumption, since it's an inexpensive, low-calorie cereal that's a nice change from oatmeal. Birds enjoy eating it in the form of dried seedling heads (millet sprays) as well as in the seed dish. Many birds, especially finches and cockatiels, can spend hours hopping or climbing over the sprays as they patiently crack open each small seed. Large hookbills may hold a spray in a claw while munching away.

The several varieties of millet are all roughly equal in nutritional value. White proso millet, the largest millet included in finch mixes, is a good size for large finches. Yellow panicum, also called finch or golden millet, is a better size for smaller finches. Some breeders are enthusiastic about Japanese millet, a medium-size brownish seed that can be purchased separately and added to seed mixes that don't include it. Red millet is a shiny seed that makes a mix look pretty, but some finches may be suspicious of it. You might want to offer a separate dish of red millet to make sure your birds are eating it before selecting a mix with a heavy proportion of that variety.

Canary seed is, as the name implies, native to the Canary Islands, where the original ancestors of our domesticated canaries came from. It's another quick energy source for small seed eaters, but it's too low in protein to be a complete diet by itself. Canary seed is not all you need to raise the next generation of healthy canaries.

Oats have received plenty of attention lately, primarily because they are high in fibers that are vital to healthy human digestion. Their tight hulls must be removed in milling, converting them to oat groats, so small birds like budgies can get at the carbo-hydrate-rich contents.

Millet, canary seed and groats could probably provide enough calories for a small bird, but they don't provide enough variety to compensate for nutritional deficiencies. Look for a mix that contains an assortment of other seeds, especially if you keep birds like cockatiels, which resist eating anything except seed. The seed possibilities include flax, sesame, rape, niger (thistle), poppy and buckwheat. A small amount of anise adds a wonderful fragrance to a seed mix.

SUNFLOWER VERSUS SAFFLOWER

Safflower and sunflower seeds are two popular oily seeds that make up the major portion of large hookbill mixes. Safflower gained popularity from mixes that boast "no sunflower."

Although considered a health food when consumed by humans, sunflower seed has developed a rather poor reputation as a result of being overfed to birds. In the bad old days, many large hookbill mixes contained nothing but sunflower seed, corn, peanuts and dried red peppers, certainly not a complete diet. Such a diet often leads to severe vitamin-A deficiencies in birds, contributing to everything from respiratory illness to egg-binding. These diseases were not caused by sunflower seed. They were caused by a lack of other nutritious foods, such as fresh fruits and vegetables. Sunflower seeds often were blamed, however.

For many years, bird owners also were disturbed by a persistent rumor that sunflower seed contained a psychoactive drug. Many people had noticed that certain imported birds, particularly Amazons, would devour sunflower seeds to the exclusion of everything else. These birds seemed addicted to sunflower seed, even though eating it exclusively resulted in ill health and greasy, dark

Fed in appropriate amounts, seed remains one of the best sources of calories (energy) for many popular species of pet birds.

plumage. I remember talking years ago with one pet store owner who wouldn't sell sunflower seeds because he thought they contained LSD. Other people said the seeds contained a narcotic related to opium. Several laboratories investigated and found nothing harmful or addictive in sunflower seeds.

I can see where the rumor started. My conures sometimes appear to be in a hypnotic trance as they merrily crack open sunflower seed after sunflower seed. I don't believe they behave like this because of any addictive ingredient inside, however, because they throw the seed to the ground as often as they eat it. I think they simply enjoy creating that satisfying crunching sound. Perhaps imported birds discover that cracking these crunchy seeds is a comforting way to work off energy or tension when confined to cages. They may continue to crack sunflower out of habit, both to soothe themselves and to ingest a relatively quick, easy-to-eat meal. In any case, because pet birds find sunflower seeds fun to eat, they may develop a tendency to eat too many of them.

I want to stress that both sunflower and safflower are grown primarily to produce oil for human consumption, not as bird food. Safflower is not a low-calorie seed, as some people seem to think. (In fact, if you're cooking with safflower oil in an effort to lose weight, get ready for a nasty surprise: A tablespoon of safflower oil has as many calories as a tablespoon of butter.)

Safflower doesn't seem to have been analyzed by bird nutritionists as extensively as sunflower seed has, but it makes a good substitute for sunflower because it offers similar nutritional value. Both seeds are a good source of calories for energy. Both are relatively good sources of plant protein. Both should be fed in moderation. In my opinion, the most important difference between the two is that safflower isn't as much fun for birds to hull, so it doesn't encourage them to stop cracking other kinds of seed.

My solution to the sunflower-versus-safflower controversy is to offer both types of seed. I switch around between different brands of seed mixes to enhance variety, but I generally select a small hookbill or cockatiel mix with no sunflower seed. Before serving the mix to my hookbills, I stir in a good

Peanuts can be used as training aids. They are best offered as a special treat to species that are prone to obesity, such as this double yellowheaded Amazon.

finch mix to add more variety and to challenge the birds by giving them smaller seeds to crack. One imported conure complained at first, probably because he was used to the easy meals he got from sunflower, but the others seem to enjoy cracking and eating the small seeds.

SPECIAL TREATS

I buy sunflower seed separately and dole it out by hand. This practice lets me monitor how much sunflower seed my conures are really eating, and it encourages them to look forward to interacting with me. You shouldn't feed more than two tablespoons of sunflower seed a day to an Amazon-size bird, and less to a smaller bird.

It isn't difficult to set limits when you're feeding by hand. A tablespoon of sunflower should be more than enough to see you through a 30-minute training session, especially if you don't count the seeds that get tossed uneaten onto the floor.

There are several different kinds of sunflower seed, including gray striped and black sunflower. The black ones, which are often seen in wild bird mixes, are smaller and don't appear to be quite as much fun for my birds to crack.

Since I give the sunflower as much for a reward as for the calories, I prefer to offer the gray striped seeds. They are available in large, medium and small sizes; the large, perfect seeds are generally sold for human consumption. I like them best because they're easy for me to hold in my fingers while moving toward a shy parrot. Always make sure that you're buying unsalted seeds.

Peanut is another oil seed that's often included in parrot mixes. It's a good source of fat and protein for underweight hookbills and young, growing birds. I don't like to see it in a mix for birds with a tendency toward obesity, such as Amazons and certain lazy conures I could mention. Like sunflower seed, it's a good high-energy treat that's probably best offered by hand or provided in very limited amounts.

Before I leave the oil-rich seeds, I should mention that fat is high in calories not because it's a bad food but because it's the single most concentrated source of food energy. During cold weather or in cooler climates, bird owners need to offer more seeds that are high in fat. A bird's fast metabolism requires extra helpings of rich food in colder weather to maintain its high body temperature (around 106°F). Unless a bird is very overweight or on a special diet designed by a veterinarian, it will probably require more fat in winter. Finches can have their mix enriched with a favorite oily seed like rape, while hookbills can indulge more in sunflower, safflower or peanuts.

OTHER SEED-MIX INGREDIENTS

Hard corn is often an ingredient in hookbill mixes. My birds will simply not eat it or even play with it, although large hookbills are said to relish it. I try to avoid mixes containing hard corn, preferring to purchase it separately for sprouting. The same conures who turn up their beaks at hard corn are positively addicted to sprouted corn, small slices of corn on the cob, or other soaked or cooked corn treats.

In general, a good hookbill mix will contain much more than the basic ingredients of sunflower or safflower seeds, peanuts and corn. Surprisingly, even the largest macaw may enjoy the tiny millet seeds. It's worth knowing that in a pinch you can make a mediocre hookbill mix better by adding a good finch mix. (In my area, good finch or cockatiel mixes are sold almost everywhere these days, but the better large hookbill mixes are usually sold only in specialty bird or pet stores.)

Other seed-mix ingredients run the gamut from buckwheat to pumpkin seed, as well as dehydrated fruits or vegetables that add some of the vitamin A that seeds generally lack. Dog kibble was once a fairly common ingredient in the better hookbill mixes, but now you can purchase pellets specifically designed for pet birds and add them yourself to make an especially nutritious mix.

Let me emphasize once more that no seed or combination of seeds contains a complete diet for a finch or parrot. My conures' diet, especially when breeding, begins with a bean mix that I cook myself. I also offer a variety of fresh fruits and vegetables in season.

The diet you offer and the proportion of seed it contains should vary depending on what kind of bird you have. As I've mentioned before, a bird of arid origin, like a cockatiel, will benefit from a much higher proportion of seed than will a rain forest bird, like an Amazon or a macaw. No single set of rules will work for all birds. It's up to you to find out what's best for your birds. You may also want to seek the nutritional advice of your avian veterinarian.

HOW FRESH IS THAT SEED?

A wild bird foraging in a natural grassland environment would probably consume some insects or insect pieces along with its seed. Bugs, moths and the other discouraging inhabitants of some seed mixes aren't necessarily bad for your birds. They may actually be a valuable source of complete protein, especially for birds like cockatiels, who may get their protein no other way.

If you're like me, however, you don't want insects loose in your house, no matter how nutritious they are! I've found that freezing seed for a full 24 hours after bringing it home is an excellent way to kill insects. Since I've started this practice, I've never awakened to a bird room full of moths.

I probably don't have to tell you not to buy old, dusty, moldy-looking seed that's buzzing with insects. However, I should probably remind you not to buy more seed than you'll use in a week or two. Seeds are designed to hold their nutritious qualities for a long time, because a season or more may pass before enough rain falls to let them sprout. Yet any food kept for a long period inevitably declines in quality. After all, you don't know how long the seed you purchased sat in a warehouse before being shipped to the store. Buying a small amount at a time from a shop with a large clientele and a fast turnover is probably the best way to guarantee that your birds will always have fresh seed.

SPROUTING SEEDS

You can check the freshness of the seed you're serving by attempting to sprout it. Fresh, nutritious seed will sprout easily, often sending out small shoots after only a day or two of soaking. Old seed won't sprout. Discard old seeds as empty calories with no nutritious value. There are two ways to sprout seed: by soaking or by planting it.

Although cockatiels are noted for their seed-loving appetites, they can learn to eat varied diets.

To check freshness, soak your seeds. Put the seeds in a jar, cover them with warm water, add a few drops of chlorine bleach (to inhibit mold), and put the jar in a dark place. Change the water every 24 hours until the seeds are sprouted to the length you want. It will take only a few days, perhaps just one or two, for the first tip to peep out of the seed. Most or all of the seeds (except for hemp, which must be sterilized to be legally sold) should sprout if they're fresh. You can serve the sprouts to your birds after you rinse them, but discard any batch that smells sour or develops mold. Peanut and corn mold are particularly dangerous, but do not feed your birds any form of mold.

I live in a hot, humid climate where I have little luck protecting soaked seeds from mold, so I prefer to plant them in sterilized potting soil. The green shoots emerge in a few days, if they're going to sprout at all, allowing me to clip them as a source of tender young greens. I've had some luck with watering (not soaking) millet sprays and watching them burst out with tiny green sprouts for my birds to enjoy. Both small seeds, like millet, and large seeds, like sunflower and corn, produce healthy, tempting sprouts that actually contain more vitamins than the original seeds. Most of my hookbills like anything green, but as I've mentioned, sprouted corn is a special favorite.

Maybe I've been lucky, but I've rarely had any difficulty getting seed to sprout — although I have had some difficulty keeping the mold from getting to it before I do. We're lucky to be living in a time when a variety of fresh, carefully selected seeds are available to enhance our birds' diet. Variety, as I've repeatedly said, is the key word here. Depending on your bird, you may be feeding seeds, pellets, fruits, vegetables, beans, rice, and even a chicken drumstick or a parrot-size slice of pizza. All these ingredients have their place in a well-balanced avian diet.

Pelleted Diets

Tom Roudybush

In recent years, more and more people have begun feeding their pet birds pelleted diets. To many, pellets are a viable alternative to seed diets or to a combination of several different foods. The real problem with pellets is that they are misunderstood. They are often put on an equal level with seeds or are treated as just another item to be added to a diet.

Some people advocate combining various brands to assure that all the nutrients present in all the brands of pellets end up in the diet. This strange method of averaging is supposed to achieve a better result than any pellet can achieve alone, but as I will explain later, pellet nutrient composition is easily manipulated. Any pellet has the potential to include all of the essential nutrients in the proper amounts. A close look at how pellets are manufactured and how pelleted diets are formulated offers a clearer idea of the real options.

HOW ARE PELLETS MADE?

Pellets are made through two primary processes. In both, materials that will compose the final pellet are ground and mixed in preparation for the pelleting process.

In the compression process, the mixed mash is cooked with steam and forced through a die, compressing the mixture into a pellet. The steam cooking changes the starch and protein in the mix from a dry powder to a stickier mix that holds together after pelleting.

In the expansion process, the mash is mixed with water, cooked under pressure and forced through a die. As the material exits the die, it expands and forms a pellet of uniform texture and a lower density than the compressed pellet. In the expansion process, the mash is cooked at higher temperatures than in the compression process. This cooks some of the fiber to the point that it becomes digestible.

Some manufacturers argue that this is an advantage, because it yields a more digestible pellet. Others argue that this increase in digestibility comes at the expense of fiber in the diet. Actually, the final composition of the pellet is what matters. Almost any composition can be achieved through either pelleting method by varying the composition of the mash and taking into account the effects of each process.

Pellets of many sizes can be produced by either of these processes. Some of the compressed pellets are pushed through closely spaced rollers and are crushed. The crushed pellets are then run over screens to yield a crumbled pellet with the fine material removed. These crumbles are available as a fine pellet for use with smaller birds. Many birds play with their food, and this variation in size and shape allows them a wider selection of forms to choose from in their recreation.

PELLET FORMULATION

The formulation of the mash that is forced into the pellet shape lies at the heart of pellet quality. Pellets are now available for a variety of animals kept under a variety of conditions. Pet stores carry pellets for rabbits, guinea pigs, hamsters and other animals. That pellets work well for these animals is a tribute to our knowledge of their needs and our understanding of the pelleting process. Few people seriously advocate the mixing of many brands of these pellets to achieve an average composition of all the brands of pellets on the market, and there is no confusion that they are simple supplements to the diets of the animals for which they were intended. They are clearly recognized as superior to a seed-only diet for any animal. The fact that pellets for birds are not afforded the same nutritional status results from our poor understanding of the use of pellets for birds.

Pellets can be formulated from virtually any ingredients. Choosing a specific composition is what distinguishes one manufacturer's product from another's. When a manufacturer makes a pellet, he first chooses the final nutrient composition he wants to see in the pellet. He decides how much of each essential nutrient needs to be present, how much fiber the diet needs, and what other materials will be added to the diet.

The manufacturer then chooses which basic materials will be used to make the mash for pelleting. The ratio of the ingredients is calculated to match the nutrient composition that was chosen as closely as possible. After this first approximation of the formulation of the diet, other nutrients can be added in relatively pure form to fill in the components that are missing or low in the mixture. Each mixture is likely to consist of some grains, some high-protein meal, and vitamin and mineral premixes. The mash is then pelleted, dried, packaged and shipped.

THE NUTRIENT COMPOSITION OF PELLETED DIETS

Some misunderstandings exist about the nutrient composition of bird pellets. Few of the nutrient requirements of birds other than poultry are known. Much of the research on the nutrient requirements of psittacine birds is known from research done in the 1980s with cockatiels at the

Pellets for birds are manufactured in the same way as pellets for other animals: by mixing a mash of foods and supplements and forcing the cooked mixture through a die. The main issue in choosing a pellet is the nutrient composition of the pellet.

Department of Avian Sciences at the University of California at Davis.

C.R. Grau and I performed a series of experiments that yielded knowledge of nutrients required by cockatiels for growth and for egg-laying. During the experiments, we tried a number of diets and measured the responses of cockatiels to these diets. We readily admit that we determined only a few of the nutrient requirements of cockatiels, but still, I am confident that we can now formulate diets for cockatiels that are adequate for most stages of their lives. I hedge on this only because we did not work on the effects of diet on specific diseases.

As an avian nutritionist, though, I have accumulated expertise that allows me to ask critical questions about avian nutrition. For example, the requirement for arginine in cockatiels is not known, but there are interrelationships between arginine and lysine in the metabolism of birds. These relationships are reasonably well known, and the lysine requirement of cockatiels for growth is known.

From this information, I can estimate the arginine requirement of cockatiels, confident that I am not so far from the actual requirement that it will cause a problem for the bird. Many such interactions of nutrients exist in nutrition. We can formulate diets for birds we have no specific information about, based on these interactions.

The possibility still exists, however, that the diet could be improved. The adequacy of the diet and the possibility that our birds' diets could be improved give us two criteria for choosing the manufacturers of the pellets we feed our birds. Choose your manufacturer based on its expertise and ability to evaluate the nutrient interactions that are important in avian nutrition.

Are pelleted diets superior to seed-only diets? From my research, I believe that a properly formulated pelleted diet is superior to a seed diet as a source of nutrition for pet birds.

Seeds alone are known to be deficient in a number of nutrients. Some of the nutrients that are likely to be lacking in seed-only diets are calcium, sodium, many of the B vitamins, some of the essential amino acids, vitamins A and D, and some of the trace minerals, such as manganese, copper and zinc. All of these, and any other nutrients, can be added to pelleted diets.

Summarizing: Pellets for birds are manufactured in the same way as pellets for other animals: by mixing a mash of foods and supplements and forcing the cooked mixture through a die. The main issue in choosing a pellet is the nutrient composition of the pellet. The most reliable way to choose a pellet for a bird is to know the qualifications of the avian nutritionist formulating the pellet and to choose a manufacturer active in research on avian nutrition.

Properly formulated pellets are a superior source of nutrition compared to seeds, because the nutrients deficient in seeds can be added to pellets in the amounts needed by the bird.

These Bourke's parakeet chicks are being exposed to a pelleted diet while they are still in the brooder.

Vitamins and Minerals

Randal N. Brue, Ph.D., and S. Blake Hawley, D.V.M.

A tremendous amount of research and attention has been devoted to vitamins and minerals in human diets over the last several years. The discovery of antioxidant and anticancer properties in beta carotene, vitamin C and vitamin E has unleashed a deluge of products for people searching for the fountain of youth and the secret to longevity.

Unfortunately, the wonderful things that vitamins and minerals do for us can backfire when certain vitamins and minerals are abused. Megadosing, which is a potentially dangerous practice among people, is even more complicated in birds because we do not know the precise minimum requirements for those species.

It is certain that vitamins and minerals play a vital and necessary role in avian nutrition. In fact, much of what we know about human nutrition today resulted from early studies involving birds, particularly poultry. Bird owners need to understand proper avian nutrition, because proper nutrition leads to pet birds with strong immune systems and good health.

WHAT ARE NUTRIENTS?

Nutrients are substances that support life by supplying energy, augmenting metabolism (chemical reactions that occur in the body), transporting substances into, through or out of the body, and acting as structural components of the body.

These are the six basic classes of nutrients: proteins (including their amino acid components), carbohydrates (simple sugars, such as glucose, and complex carbohydrates, such as starch and fiber), fats, vitamins, minerals and water.

Birds require varying amounts of nutrients, depending on their functions, their interactions with each other and their physiological state. Essential nutrients are those that the body requires to drive necessary biochemical reactions. They must be supplied by food because the bird's body cannot synthesize them.

Currently, we recognize 40 individual nutrients as essential in the avian diet. With some notable exceptions, most of these compounds are all naturally present, in widely varying amounts, in the ingredients that make up a diet. Regrettably, however, they often tend to be present at levels below those required for optimum health. Typically, a bird that is marginally deficient in one or more nutrients will appear very normal and

Egg yolks are one of the best sources of vitamin A, but they should be fed to birds with caution because of the possibility of spoilage.

"healthy" until the insidious effects of malnutrition take their toll, sometimes resulting in illness and death.

A COMPLEMENTARY DIET

One of the goals of dietary formulation is to select ingredients that complement one another nutritionally. Each ingredient has a unique nutritional profile, with certain nutrients being present in abundant quantities, while others occur in only meager amounts or are only partially available to the body.

Once you have selected the best possible complement of ingredients, you must conduct a critical evaluation of the overall nutrient profile to determine remaining deficiencies. Only then can you add the proper supplementation to achieve a balanced and effective diet. You can apply this process to any type of diet, whether it be during the formulation of a commercial, processed diet, a nutrient fortified seed-based diet or a diet consisting of a wide variety of grains, seeds, vegetables and other food items. In any case, the diet must contain the proper quantities of supplemental vitamins and minerals if you expect it to support the long term health of the bird.

Of the common nutritional problems in pet birds, the most frequent and potentially devastating to the bird are vitamin deficiencies (specifically of vitamins A and D_3) and mineral deficiencies (primarily of calcium). Vitamins are organic compounds that the body requires in minute quantities for normal metabolic or physiologic functions. When their presence in the diet is limited or unavailable, specific characteristic deficiency syndromes result. Minerals, on the other hand, are inorganic substances that fulfill three basic functions: They serve as structural components of the body, electrolyte components of fluids and tissues, and catalysts or components of enzyme, hormone or other biological complexes.

Moist foods can be dusted with a high-quality multivitamin powder. Follow directions when adding vitamins to your bird's soft foods to prevent overdoses.

THE FAT-SOLUBLE VITAMINS

Vitamins are necessary for normal functioning of the body and for regulating a tremendous variety of physiologic processes. They are divided into two general classes: fat-soluble vitamins (A, D, E, K), which are transported and stored along with fat in the body, and water-soluble vitamins (B complex and C), which essentially are not stored in the body and therefore must reliably be provided on a daily basis.

The classic seed-only diets that have historically been the pet bird's mainstay are moderately deficient in most vitamins and are extremely deficient in vitamins A and D_3. Unsupplemented seed diets are guaranteed to cause health problems eventually, and can result in the death of a bird because of the severe deficiencies of these two critical vitamins.

Healthy birds require vitamin A in their diets. Probably best known for its function in the physiology of vision, vitamin A is also necessary for the growth and differentiation of epithelial tissues, especially the alimentary (gut), respiratory and genitourinary tracts. Its function in bone growth and the maintenance of normal reproduction is also documented. To add to this impressive list, vitamin A is generally thought to improve immune function by increasing production and differentiation of immune cells.

Because hand-feeding formula manufacturers have already considered the vitamin and mineral needs of growing chicks, adding vitamins and minerals to a processed hand-feeding diet is risky and possibly lethal.

Not only does vitamin A enhance the immune function, it also plays a crucial role in preventing disease-causing organisms from entering the body by maintaining mucus membranes and secretory tissues. Lack of vitamin A results in hyperkeratosis (hypertrophy or overgrowth) and squamous metaplasia (a change in the normal type of cell present) of these tissues. These tissue alterations commonly result in diseases such as bacterial, fungal or viral infections or kidney damage. Besides squamous metaplasia (frequently observed as small white nodules, pustules and swellings in the mouth) and hyperkeratosis (which may appear as a thickened scale area on the feet), hypovitaminosis A (a condition caused by the deficiency of vitamin A) may result in general weakness and poor feather condition, eye problems, reproductive problems (reduced production and early embryonic death) and poor immune function.

Vitamin A is not found in its active form in plants. Instead, it occurs as vitamin precursors, namely the carotenoid pigments. Of this large group of natural plant pigments, beta carotene is the most common, and it yields the highest amount of vitamin A upon biotransformation. Plants high in carotene include all dark orange vegetables (carrots, sweet potatoes and red peppers) and dark green, leafy vegetables (spinach, kale and parsley). Light colored

produce contains very low amounts.

Most fruits are extremely low to moderate in their content of vitamin A activity. Commonly available items such as apples, bananas and grapes are particularly low. The best fruit sources for vitamin A include apricots, kiwis and papaya. Of all the grain products, corn provides the best level, although it is only moderate. One of the best sources of vitamin A is egg yolk, but feed this with caution because of the possibility of spoilage.

Most fortified seed-based diets have been adequately supplied with vitamin A. Because the ultimate success of the diet depends on both the formulation and intake of the supplement, limiting the portion offered and monitoring intake of ingredients may be helpful. If the diet or the intake of its supplement is questioned, the addition of foods with high vitamin A activity is recommended. Any moist foods can also be dusted with a high-quality multivitamin product, being careful to follow the product's directions to avoid excessive intakes. It must be realized that this method leaves much to chance, since the intake of the vitamins is not guaranteed.

Most formulated diets (extruded or pelleted types) contain adequate amounts of vitamin A and therefore must not be supplemented with vitamin mixes. Because vitamin A is a fat-soluble vitamin, it is stored efficiently in the body (primarily in the liver) and is not easily eliminated. Extremely high levels of vitamin A may result in a toxicity. Signs of hypervitaminosis A include bone abnormalities, tissue inflammation, or yellowing of the skin and liver dysfunction. Beta carotene is converted to vitamin A only when the body needs it, so it is virtually impossible to overdose on this vitamin-A precursor from plant sources. Instead, the excessive levels of stored pigment will discolor the skin and fat.

An all-seed diet or any diet composed only of plant-source foods lacks vitamin D_3

(cholecalciferol). Plant sources contain vitamin D in the form of the compound ergocalciferol, or vitamin D_2. Although mammals can use this particular form, avian species cannot. Vitamin D_3 is synthesized in the body by exposure to sufficient ultraviolet light obtained through outdoor sunlight. Most pet birds, however, live indoors, so they require vitamin D_3 in their diets.

The most important role of vitamin D is the enhancement of calcium absorption and its regulation of calcium and phosphorus homeostasis (the normal stabilizing of these two minerals in the body), a complex process responsible for ensuring the right amount of each mineral so that bone forms properly and cells function normally. Vitamin D_3 is clearly necessary for proper bone formation. A deficiency of this vitamin causes rickets in nestlings, which is marked by bending and distortion of the bones, and osteomalacia, which is softening of the bone because of insufficient mineralization in adults.

Hypocalcemic tetany (seizures, especially when frightened) is the most commonly recognized form of vitamin D deficiency in pet birds. This is often seen in African grey parrots that are maintained on calcium- and vitamin D_3-deficient seed/plant-origin diets. Contrary to popular belief, African greys do not appear to have a significantly higher requirement for calcium; however, they show the signs of calcium deficiency more readily and more blatantly than other avian species because of apparent differences in their ability to mobilize the calcium stored in bone. Other problems caused by an insufficient supply of vitamin D include liver, gastrointestinal tract and kidney diseases.

Just as with vitamin A, hypervitaminosis D can cause a diseased state too. Vitamin D intoxication results in soft tissue mineralization, especially in the kidneys and the digestive tract. Anorexia, lameness, lethargy, diarrhea and decreased reproductive performance have been seen in birds that receive high levels of vitamin D in their diets. There is also evidence suggesting that baby blue-and-gold macaws may be more prone to hypervitaminosis D than other species.

Vitamin E, a compound of plant origins, is most important to birds in the form of alpha-tocopherol. Its primary function is as a biological antioxidant, maintaining cell membrane integrity by scavenging free radicals, which are the harmful byproducts of metabolism. Alpha-tocopherol may also help boost the immune system by stimulating antibody production, and by increasing the activity of immune cells.

Although it rarely occurs, vitamin E deficiency causes neuromuscular problems, such as encephalomalacia or "crazy chick" disease; vascular problems, such as exudative diathesis in which fluids pool in the body tissues; and reproductive problems, including decreased fertility and embryo viability. This

Vitamin A protects against infections and is found in an all-time favorite food of many pet birds — corn.

latter deficiency manifestation may be somewhat more common since the vitamin E requirement for maximum reproduction may be higher than the bird's general requirement. Cockatiels also display a vitamin E-responsive syndrome in which muscle weakness and wing paralysis is seen.

Excessive vitamin E levels are also extremely uncommon because this vitamin is simply not very toxic. It is possible that at very high levels, vitamin E may affect the absorption of other fat-soluble vitamins and thus exert a indirect negative effect.

Vitamin K is derived from green plants (vitamin K_1) and bacteria (vitamin K_2) and is necessary for the synthesis of blood clotting factors that are needed for normal clotting and fluidity. Although most diets by themselves are marginal in their supply, bacterial synthesis in the gastrointestinal tract will generally help fulfill the bird's need. A bird will not usually be deficient in vitamin K unless it undergoes prolonged antibiotic therapy that limits normal bacterial flora in the gut, or it has severe liver disease, which causes reduced absorption. A deficiency may result in anemia or prolonged bleeding, such as seen in "conure bleeding syndrome."

THE WATER-SOLUBLE VITAMINS

The B-complex vitamins (thiamin, riboflavin, niacin, pyridoxine, pantothenic acid, biotin, folic acid, B_{12} and choline) act as coenzymes involved in energy production, nutrient utilization and metabolism. They also play a role in appetite. Deficiencies, which are seen less commonly because many foods contain good to adequate amounts, generally result in nonspecific signs, such as anorexia, weight loss, paralysis, loss of coordination, poor feathering, poor hatchability and retarded growth. This makes identification of a specific deficiency almost impossible in an adult bird. Any of these broad signs

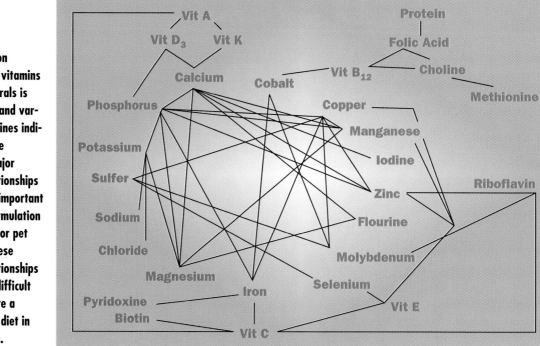

Interaction between vitamins and minerals is complex and varied. The lines indicate some of the major interrelationships that are important in the formulation of diets for pet birds. These interrelationships make it difficult to prepare a balanced diet in the home.

should elicit an evaluation of the diet and adequate supplementation of all the B-complex vitamins, rather than attempting to determine the specific vitamin at fault.

Birds need vitamin C to synthesize collagen, which means it is essential in proper cell structure and integrity, and in bone formation. Vitamin C is also an exceptional antioxidant, and it has been shown to decrease embryonic mortality, to improve fertility and to boost the immune system during times of stress. With the exception of a few highly specialized species (the red vented bulbul and willow ptarmigan), birds do not require vitamin C in their diets because their bodies synthesize it from glucose. Deficiencies of vitamins A, E and biotin, as well as disease, can impair this biosynthesis, however. Although toxicity is unlikely, megadosing may overstimulate the enzyme responsible for its degradation, but moderate levels are probably beneficial and certainly do not cause harm.

For birds on supplemented seed diets or processed diets, additional vitamin supplementation is discouraged except in the form of natural foods, such as vegetables, grains and small amounts of fruits. The hand-fed chick is especially susceptible to vitamin overdosing. Because the metabolism of the growing chick differs significantly from the adult, adding vitamins or minerals to processed hand-feeding diets is risky at best and possibly lethal. For this reason, do not add additional vitamins and minerals to processed hand-feeding diets.

MEET THE MACRO MINERALS

Minerals are a very small but significant part of the avian diet. The macro minerals are necessary for the body's structural integrity and egg production (in the case of calcium and phosphorus) and for maintaining acid/base and body fluid balance

(sodium, potassium and chlorine). The trace or micro minerals serve as components of metalloenzymes responsible for driving an incredible number of biochemical reactions. Minerals, however, should not be considered as individuals, but rather as a group because of their complex interactions and potential for harm when imbalanced. As the intake level of a mineral (or minerals) rises above the requirement, toxic amounts can accumulate in the body, or the mineral may bind other minerals, which prevents absorption and can lead to a deficiency.

A problem quickly arises in avian nutrition because of the small quantities of calcium and phosphorus in a seed-only diet, especially in breeding birds. Bird owners often assume incorrectly that supplementation

Vitamin C, found in both spinach and oranges, is necessary for building collagen, the primary element of cartilage.

The classic seed-only diets that have historically been a pet bird's mainstay are moderately deficient in most vitamins and are extremely lacking in vitamins A and D$_3$.

with a cuttlebone will totally alleviate a calcium deficiency. In fact, this is not the case, since the primary assumption is that the bird will eat enough cuttlebone to meet its calcium needs. This may occur, but the concurrent deficiency of vitamin D$_3$ prevents adequate absorption of the calcium consumed.

Calcium homeostasis is a complex subject. It is regulated and affected by active vitamin D$_3$, plasma calcium levels, phosphorus, parathyroid hormone and calcitonin. To further complicate the picture, protein content, certain compounds in the diet (oxalates and phytates) and concentrations of free fatty acids all may have negative effects on intestinal absorption of calcium.

The ideal ratio of calcium to available phosphorus should be 2:1 for proper bone development and maintenance. The amount of phosphorus that is actually available to the bird varies depending on the dietary ingredients and must be considered in the evalu-

ation of the diet. Phosphorus from inorganic sources and animal products is nearly 100 percent available, while that from plants and their products is often only about 30 percent available. In periodic producers (such as pet birds), this ratio is also considered ideal for normal reproductive performance. For this reason, the diet must be balanced.

Calcium levels in most seed, grain and other plant sources are grossly deficient, with levels in the range of 0.02 to 0.1 percent. Although this is adequate to keep a mature bird alive, it will not keep that bird healthy! Young, growing birds that receive these levels will show decreased growth and weak, pliable bones. Our research has shown the optimum requirements for pet birds to be in the range of 0.3 to 0.5 percent for adults and 0.7 to 1.0 percent for growing birds.

Mineral supplements, such as oyster shell and cuttlebone, supply calcium in the form of calcium carbonate (38 percent Ca).

A bird that nutritionally craves calcium will definitely seek out and consume supplements but will seldom eat the proper amounts. This, compounded with the probable deficiency of vitamin D_3, makes achieving ideal balance very difficult if the bird does not receive a processed-type diet. Excesses are only encountered with overzealous supplementation of calcium, especially when accompanied with adequate or generous levels of vitamin D_3. This usually occurs with poorly formulated processed diets or gross misuse of supplemental products. To avoid these problems, do not supplement processed diets.

Sodium, chlorine and potassium levels rarely create distinct deficiency symptoms, although typical diets often supply them in marginal amounts. Excesses may occur with liberal use of mineral supplements. Excessive levels result in decreased growth and appetite loss, increased water intake and subsequent polyuria, poor feathering and cartilage problems in chicks.

TRACING THE MICRO MINERALS

The essential trace minerals are of equal importance as a group, though in micro quantities. Mineral levels in the foods are influenced by the mineral levels of the soil on which they were grown. Of the trace minerals, iodine deficiencies have been the most frequently encountered, particularly in budgerigars, because of the extremely low levels of iodine in the foods typically offered to them (millet and canary grass seed) and the subsequent ease of goiter development.

Most foodstuffs that pet birds eat contain marginal supplies of iron, copper, zinc, manganese and selenium, but like the B-complex vitamins, their levels are sufficient to prevent distinct, pronounced deficiency signs in adult birds.

Rather, they will manifest themselves as generalized, nonspecific problems such as poor feathering, decreased disease resistance, lethargy and depressed appetite. Occasionally, anemia will be observed.

Toxicity of the trace minerals is infrequent, with the possible exception of iron. Because the body has no way to rid itself of excess iron except through bleeding, high amounts, in conjunction with stress, disease, heredity and possibly other, as yet unknown factors, may result in liver damage. This condition, known as hemochromatosis or iron storage disease, is most common in softbilled birds (e.g. mynahs, toucans and touracos). It has, however, been occasionally observed in a variety of psittacine species.

Selection of foods that are good sources of minerals and trace minerals, plus any necessary supplementation, is essential to produce an adequate diet. A well-researched formulated diet will eliminate these problems.

TO SUPPLEMENT OR NOT TO SUPPLEMENT

As discussed earlier, the great difficulty with supplementation is to achieve, not upset, the delicate balance between all of the interrelated minerals. This can be very challenging, if not impossible, to accomplish fully. A well-researched, carefully formulated processed diet can easily eliminate these problems and help provide balanced nutrient intake.

Although a very complex and detailed subject, the vitamin and mineral nutrition of pet birds can be improved by learning about foods and ingredients that are good dietary components. The fate of pet birds, both today and tomorrow, lies in our increased knowledge and enhanced research efforts in understanding and elucidating their nutritional needs. Every bird owner must accept the responsibility for providing superior nutrition (not over-nutrition) to help guarantee a long life for his or her pet bird.

Finicky Eaters

Nancy R. Sondel

Does your darling avian pet sulk or throw a tantrum each time you offer it cantaloupe, carrots or pellets? Although most canaries and finches readily accept new foods, many psittacines (parrot-type birds) require consistent, long-term coaxing. Developing or improving your bird's eating habits depends not only on your bird's attitude, but on yours as well. If you would like your bird to eat a balanced diet, resolve to attain that goal no matter how long it takes. Supplement this commitment by learning the psychology of food as perceived by your feathered companion.

MOTIVATION

Some birds will accept vegetables more readily if they are served in unusual ways. This severe macaw is enjoying zucchini, yellow squash and carrot served on a cable tie.

What motivates a bird to eat? Hunger is a factor, but certainly not the only one. At least four other factors influence a bird's attitude toward food. The first is visual appeal. A bird's senses of taste and smell are minimal compared to ours, but its eyesight is exceptional. Birds are initially attracted to a food's color, size and shape. Colorful foods include: green peppers, peas, broccoli, spinach and other dark leafy greens; red beets, peppers and

cabbage; carrots, cantaloupe, yams, papaya and oranges; yellow corn and winter squash. To tempt your bird, combine three or four colors to provide a visual feast. Also, foods like broccoli and corn on the cob have interesting textures that attract birds visually and stimulate them to pick at, and eventually eat, the foods.

Stringy spaghetti squash, broccoli and corn on the cob also provide entertainment or activity, the second motivating factor. (Discard remaining corncobs so your bird won't ingest them.) Like intelligent young children, birds explore and play with their food. Spear fruits and vegetables on an avian shish-kebab skewer, homemade or commercially manufactured, that hangs in the cage.

Birds naturally like to sort through their food and play with it while eating, which means they are bound to waste some. Don't be discouraged. Simply serve smaller portions until they show a like or dislike for particular food items.

Flock instincts are a third factor that strongly influences birds' eating habits, especially psittacines. Throughout their lives, birds enjoy closeness and companionship at mealtime. Their interest in food is heightened when they see another bird – or their beloved owner – eating. For birds, eating is a social event. In the beginning, one or both parents feed their babies by regurgitating food. Weanlings and fledglings acquire eating habits by imitating parents and flock members. In the wild, adult birds often forage together for food. During courtship, males regurgitate to feed their mates, and the cycle begins again.

When a bird bonds with you, you become its "flock." Your tame bird will want to

Try a Tempting Shish-Kebab
For a fun, nutritious treat, cut up a few of your bird's favorite fruits and vegetables in medium-sized chunks and spear them on a skewer (either homemade or commercially manufactured). The convenient kebab skewers, available at avian supply stores or through mail order in avian magazines, hang from the inside top of the cage to provide healthy treats and super exercise.

eat with you, just as it would with a member of its own species. To tempt your bird, don't simply set food in its dish and walk away. Bring your feathered pal out of its cage; eat, pretend to eat, or feed another human (or avian role model) while your bird watches. Chew with your mouth wide open, and exclaim loudly while making lip-smacking sounds. Exaggerate! Your worst table manners will be the most convincing.

When your bird becomes curious, offer food in your hand, and pretend to eat from it. Or, while an enthusiastic bird eats out of your hand, offer some to the reluctant eater, then pass it back to the good eater. After a few rounds, the uninitiated bird will not want to be left out.

Finally, birds are motivated by habit. For this reason, introduce new foods at your bird's natural feeding times when it is most receptive: early morning and sundown. If your bird resists, offer only the new food, withholding familiar food for several hours.

A bird's strongly developed instincts and habits may cause it to reject anything that it perceives as unusual. For example, if you usually hang greens from the cage bars, but decide to switch them to a food dish,

your bird may suddenly ignore them. The same is true if you replace or relocate a food dish in the cage.

OFFER VARIETY

If your bird won't accept new foods, variety is the answer. First, vary the location of the food. If you want your bird to eat dark leafy greens, try hanging them from the cage-top. If this doesn't work, spear the greens on a favorite toy or perch, or weave them through the cage bars. To tempt a bird that likes to bathe, place sopping-wet greens on the cagetop, clean cage floor, kitchen counter or other play area. Initially, your bird may eat greens only if they are in the "right" location.

Second, entice your bird by varying the appearance of the food. A carrot, for example, may be fed raw (grated, chopped, diced or sliced into thin strips), steamed (crisp or mashed) or juiced. Some birds will accept food in one form but will refuse it in every other form. Do grated carrots taste different than chopped carrots? No, but they look and feel different, which is what matters to your bird.

Experiment with size, but keep it proportionate. Large parrots often like long, narrow food chunks to hold in their feet. Small psittacines may appreciate scaled-down bits. Don't overwhelm a tiny budgie by dangling huge greens or other items in front of its face, especially if the food is unfamiliar. When you introduce new food to your small or medium bird, offer an unintimidating morsel between your fingertips – a single grain of cooked rice, a thin sliver of apple or grated carrot, or a petite broccoli floret.

When varying the food's appearance, be adventurous. Don't limit yourself to preparing food the way humans usually enjoy it. My aviary budgies used to eat broccoli florets, always leaving the chopped stalks. Since the budgies were accustomed to grated carrots and beets, I tried grating the broccoli stalks. As strange as this preparation appeared to me, it apparently appealed to my birds, who now eat all their broccoli enthusiastically.

On the other hand, your bird may prefer crunchy stalks. The bright stalks and veins of beet tops and red chard are particularly attractive. Hang them whole, or chop them. When you offer dandelion greens and spinach to your small bird, be sure it has access to the chewy stems.

If your bird won't touch oranges or green peppers, hang a thick piece of nutritious pulp in its cage. The soft, chewy texture may appeal to your birds. While not considered tasty by most humans, pulps and stalks encourage some birds to try other parts of the fruits and vegetables.

Although your bird has relatively few taste buds, there are at least two ways to heighten flavor. First, add untraditional or pungent flavoring. One of my budgies, for example, refuses certain raw vegetables unless they are spiked with lemon juice. Salsa may entice larger parrots.

Warming food also enhances flavor. If your bird doesn't like raw broccoli, for example, try steaming it slightly.

To sneak nutritious foods into your bird's diet, add them to baked goods. If your bird eats bread or muffins, mix in any of the following: mashed squash, yams, sweet potatoes or tofu; ground-up avian pellets; cooked cereals (oatmeal, cream of buckwheat); pureed baby food from jars (carrots, peas and other vegetables); eggs, low-fat cottage cheese, brewer's yeast or peanut butter (in very small amounts). Nutritious breads and muffins aren't a substitute for a varied diet, but they are a good supplement and transition food.

Other treats like toast, unsalted crackers, grapes and apples aren't particularly high in nutrition, but many birds readily accept them. For birds with a rigid eating pattern, these snacks may provide a turning point. Once a bird tries a new food, it usually is willing to try others.

THE IMPORTANCE OF A GOOD DIET

Avian veterinarians attribute at least 90 percent of illness and disease in pet birds to inadequate nutrition. Since seeds lack up to half the nutrients pet birds need daily, they must obtain the rest from other sources. If you introduce a major dietary change, be sure your bird is fully weaned and in good health. Have your bird examined by an avian vet, who will show you how to monitor your bird's weight during the dietary transition.

Besides offering nutritious table food, there are two effective ways to supplement a seed diet. One is to mix a powdered vitamin/mineral supplement with your bird's soft food (grated carrots or apples, for example) in small portions that will be completely consumed.

NUTRITIOUS PELLETS

The second alternative is to teach your bird to eat avian pellets. Pellets are well-balanced, convenient and easy to measure. Some people, however, have difficulty getting their birds to recognize pellets as a source of food. Mixing pellets in a dish with seed is rarely successful, because a bird can ignore or discard the pellets.

A safe way to introduce pellets is to combine them with familiar food to which they adhere. First, moisten pellets with water, or orange or carrot juice. Then add the pellets to your bird's favorite soft foods: cooked brown rice, soggy whole-wheat bread, mashed tofu or sweet potatoes. As your bird continually sees and touches the pellets in the "mash," it will learn that pellets are food.

When your bird has accepted the mash, gradually moisten the pellets less. Decrease the table food in the mixture so the pellets crumble and begin to resemble those in the feed dish. (If your bird doesn't already eat table food, mix a little seed with the moistened pellets instead.)

Meanwhile, permanently substitute dry pellets for seed in all the feed dishes. Start at night when your bird goes to sleep. In the morning when your bird is hungry, offer only water, dry pellets (in the "seed" dish), pellet mash, and a few vegetables or greens. Encourage your bird to eat the pellets (dry or mashed) as you play together with the food. Present avian or human role models, as discussed earlier. Freshen the food supply every few hours, but do not provide seed until early or mid-afternoon. Offer seed in a new feed dish or in your hand.

Give your bird a few minutes to eat the seed, then remove it. Replenish the table food and pellets, withholding seed until just before your bird goes to sleep. Repeat this procedure for two to three days. Then, instead of offering seed in the afternoon, wait until just after sundown.

By now, your bird will probably be eating other nourishing food instead of waiting all day for seed. Every few days, increase the time between seed feedings.

If you are converting your bird from seed to a pelleted diet, the next step is to

offer seed only once on alternate days, then less often. Eventually, birds on pelleted diets may enjoy seed as an occasional treat or a daily "after-dinner dessert." Pellet-eating birds also benefit physically and psychologically from daily moderate servings of fruits and vegetables.

The pellet mash and gradual conversion were highly successful with my 50 adult budgies, a species that is notoriously (and infuriatingly) resistant to change. Regardless of the methods you use, expect birds to vary in their adaptability. Some accept new foods immediately; others take weeks, months or, occasionally, years. Whether you are introducing table food or pellets to a seed-dependent bird, be firm, consistent, observant and supportive. Don't give up or regard your bird's resistance as a sign of inadequate intelligence. Consider our own species' reluctance to adopt healthier eating patterns!

This chapter cannot address every situation, but you may pinpoint a solution if you remember these principles: First, birds are motivated to eat for a variety of reasons; second, their food may be presented in a variety of ways.

Respond to your bird's instincts and temperament with patience, persistence, flexibility and creativity. A balanced diet may add years to your bird's life — and treasured avian companionship to your own.

Broccoli has an interesting texture that many birds, including this young blue-and-gold macaw, find appealing.

Healthy Snacks

Denise Testa

What your mother always said still holds true, not only for you but also for your bird: Healthy foods are nature's best preventive medicine. This doesn't just include regular meals; it also covers those in-between snacks and treats.

You can use quality treats with high food value as rewards, to build trust, or to add interest and excitement to your bird's day. Naturally healthy goodies cover a wide range, from the simple to the exotic. Often we overlook delicious but unfamiliar foods that will satisfy even the most discerning avian tastes.

If you share food with your bird, be sure to give it its own portion, because bacteria and germs from your mouth can be harmful to your pet.

In addition to good nutrition and flavor, make sure that what you serve your bird looks as good as it tastes. No matter how vitamin-packed and yummy a treat is, it must look appetizing to your bird. Fascinating textures along with intriguing colors are good ways to entice your bird into sampling something new.

FRESH FACTS

Fresh fruits and vegetables make great treats even if you're already serving them as part of your bird's meal. Keep in mind that the fresher the produce, the more nutritious and tastier it is. If you have a garden, you're ahead of the game. If you don't, perhaps a friend or relative who does will help out. Another option is locating local farmer's markets and fruit stands, which generally will provide you with fresher fruits and vegetables than most supermarkets. Natural food stores are also a good choice because they often stock organically grown produce.

Organically grown produce is preferable if available. You can serve it whole because you don't have to peel it to remove poisonous spray residues that may have permeated the skin. This is important, because in the case of many vegetables, the skin is one of the most nutritious parts.

A VARIETY OF VEGGIES

Throughout the year, many different vegetables are available that will add variety to your bird's life. Carrots are power packs of calcium and vitamins A and B, so try tempting your bird to nibble by leaving the tops on. Another veggie that's loaded with vitamin A is the sweet potato. Although it will never win any beauty contests, you can compensate by offering just the skins, especially if they are creatively peeled. It's difficult for most inquisitive birdies to turn down at least a bite of curlicued peel.

Hot peppers are also a fiery favorite of many winged gourmets. They are so popular there's even an entire family of chili peppers commonly known as "bird peppers" because of the attraction they have for wild birds. Another crowd pleaser, especially in our household, is sweet corn. Even though it contains only a moderate amount of vitamin A compared to dark-green veggies such as kale and spinach, sweet corn seems to be much more readily accepted and consumed by all sizes of the feathered set. Brussels sprouts also work as avian appetizers. These "miniature cabbage heads" have vitamins C and B, plus minerals such as iron and potassium. They also offer plenty of entertainment for mid- and large-sized parrots that enjoy the challenge of shredding them.

LUSCIOUS FRUITS

As for fruits, serve your bird apricots for their high quantity of vitamin A and sweet flavor. For substantial amounts of calcium, dates get top billing. Whole dates lack a bit in the looks department, so cut them

> Try this recipe, and see if your bird agrees that it's a real treat.
>
> ### Veggie Dazzler
>
> 2 cups unsweetened
>   pineapple juice
> 1 slice lemon
> 2 medium carrots
>   (washed, scraped and cut into
>   small pieces)
> 1 cup crushed ice
>
> Blend juice, carrots and lemon slice until the carrots are liquefied. Add crushed ice, and continue to blend until ice is pureed. Garnish with orange slices and enjoy.

into chewy, bite-size pieces for "beak food." A relative newcomer to the scene is kiwi fruit. It tastes like an exotic blend of strawberry, pineapple and banana, but contains three to four times more vitamin C than an orange (on a pound-for-pound basis). The kiwi's bright-green interior is a natural for being served in slices or chunks.

Probably the most tried-and-true fruit treat given to birds is the grape. Its compact size and juicy sweet taste make it a perennial favorite. Although grapes don't have nearly as much nutritional value as the other fruits

Give your bird an occasional nut as a treat, and offer the snack to your pet in its shell, because fishing the nutmeat out provides good mental stimulation.

Juices, nectars or coolers made from fruits and vegetables provide refreshingly tangy tastes and beautiful colors, and they can be shared safely with your birds!

mentioned, you can compensate. Grapes are great for sneaking in extra vitamin A. Simply hollow out a channel in the grape by using a toothpick. Then prick a small hole into the soft gelatin vitamin A capsule and squeeze out a drop or two into the grape. (Discard any partially used capsules immediately.) Not only can you feel better about serving nutritionally improved grapes, but your bird will appreciate the delicious snack.

Dried fruit is a tasty alternative if fresh is difficult to find. Make sure that it is naturally dried and unsulfurated, though. If the fruit looks a little darker than you expected, don't worry; this is because you are used to dried fruits that have had the color and texture preserved artificially. You can soak dried fruit briefly in water to tenderize it, or just serve as is; your bird will enjoy it either way.

'GOING NUTS' THE SENSIBLE WAY

Nuts and seeds are without doubt convenient high-energy snacks; however, they are also high in fat and should be given only in moderation. Nuts are actually hard-shelled seeds, and all seeds are a rich source of the B vitamins, vitamin E and the minerals phos-

phorus and iron. With the exception of almonds and sesame seeds, most nuts and seeds lack calcium. This is another good reason why they should be limited to a "treats only" basis.

Our birds usually have their pasta raw, but on special occasions we serve them this:

Pasta a'la Parrot Primavera

2 ears fresh sweet corn
1 bunch asparagus
2 to 3 handfuls snow peas
2 red bell peppers

Almost any of your bird's favorite fresh veggies will taste great in this recipe, so feel free to substitute or add to the ingredients given. Gather together the vegetables of choice, wash them carefully, and slice them into birdie bite-size pieces. Steam them over medium heat until they are slightly tender but still crisp. Spoon the veggies on top of flavored pasta, and let your bird experience a taste sensation.

Because of their high fat content, nuts and seeds can become rancid if kept in a warm or damp place. Store them in the refrigerator or freezer where they will keep almost indefinitely. Never give your bird salted nuts or seeds.

Most common nuts contain approximately 10 to 25 percent protein. Pine nuts (pignolias) have the highest percentage, closely followed by peanuts, pistachios and almonds. If you do give nuts as a treat, serve them still in the shell. For smaller beaks, you may want to "start" the shell with a nutcracker. Fishing the nutmeat out provides good mental stimulation for many birds.

Seeds can play an important part in your bird's life. The grain known as millet has a delicate flavor but contains a complete protein and little starch. Its close relative, spray millet, also has these attributes as well as being on a stem that's handy to hang onto while being consumed. Both make excellent treats for small to medium birds. For the larger bird, pumpkin seeds are a good choice. Not only are they rich in potassium and vitamin B, but they have a higher content of iron than any other seed. So when you're carving out that Halloween pumpkin, save the seeds, dry them in your oven and let your bird celebrate with a tasty treat.

NOT JUST FOR THE BIRDS

If your bird has a "sweet beak" or merely wants in on what everyone else is eating, don't worry. Plenty of delicious and nutritious treats are appropriate for sharing. (If you share your food with your bird, make sure to give your pet its own portion; never expose your bird to the germs and bacteria in your mouth.)

During the hot, humid days of summer, a cool beverage is the perfect way to quench an avian or human thirst. Juices, nectars or coolers made from fruits and vegetables provide refreshingly tangy tastes, as well

Almonds add calcium to a bird's diet.

as beautiful colors. You can use one ingredient to make a fresh juice cocktail, or blend together a whole harvest. The key to concocting an array of delicious drinks is: Think healthy, use what's fresh and be creative.

If your bird favors more international cuisine, try flavored pasta, which can be given either raw or cooked. Spinach, beet, tomato and carrot are some of the traditional pasta flavorings; however, exotic combinations are available such as Thai Chili Peanut Pasta, which our parrots consider a "bodacious goody." The various shapes and sizes the pasta comes in also add to the snacking enjoyment. Natural-food stores are good places for locating flavored pasta made with healthy ingredients and no preservatives.

Many commerical treats blended especially for pet birds are available. Some are definitely better than others. Make sure to study the ingredients and how the mix was prepared. Be careful of additives and overprocessing. Know what you are giving your bird because birds are what they eat.

Avian Obesity

Jeanne Smith, D.V.M.

O besity is a condition commonly seen in pet birds. It is also sometimes seen in aviary or breeding birds. Obesity is defined as an excessive accumulation and storage of body fat and is caused by an imbalance between energy (calorie) intake and energy used. More calories are ingested than are being burned up by the bird, so the extra calories are stored as fat. Therefore, a bird may become obese because of inactivity or a high-calorie diet. This is why pet birds are more prone to obe-sity than aviary birds: Pet birds tend to be less active and are often given high-calorie treats or "people food."

RECOGNIZING AN OBESE BIRD

Obesity is easier to recognize in pet birds than in aviary birds because pets are observed more closely and handled more frequently; however, the same clinical signs can be seen in an aviary bird when examined.

A bird generally stores fat first in its ab-

One way to combat obesity in your pet bird is to offer it healthy treats, such as fruits and vegetables.

domen, along its sides between the abdomen and thighs, and around the top of its breast or the clavicle area. Later it may also start filling stores in its "chin" area and under the skin throughout its body.

When you observe an obese bird from a distance, you may notice that the abdomen between the breast and the base of the tail bulges downward and appears rounded. You may also notice that the bird stands with its legs spread farther apart than other birds.

Another sign of obesity may be a balding appearance. Feathers grow in tracts or patches on the skin. As fat accumulates under the skin, these tracts spread apart, leaving some bare skin exposed. A fairly obvious clue that your bird is obese is a bulging "double chin" under its lower beak, with no feathers over the bulging skin. Other clues may be a reluctance to fly or inability to gain altitude when flying.

Some birds actually become anorexic and stop eating because of obesity. In aviary or breeding birds, infertility or egg binding in the female can be additional signs of obesity.

Physical examination of the bird will confirm a diagnosis of obesity. Soft, pale yellow pads under the skin or abdominal muscles are excess fat deposits. Body weight can be a clue, although weight alone is not a good diagnostic tool, because there can be quite a bit of variation in body size and normal body weights for a number of bird species. A physical examination may also detect lipomas, which are benign fatty tumors found in various places under the skin. These may be removed surgically, or they may be monitored during a weight-loss program. Lipomas often disappear by the time the bird has returned to a normal weight.

TREATING OBESITY

Obesity can be treated through a weight-reduction program that increases the bird's activity level and/or reduces the bird's

caloric intake. Consult your avian veterinarian or an experienced breeder (familiar with your bird's species) to determine an appropriate target weight for your bird, taking into account the size of its body frame as well as the normal range for its species. You should make arrangements to weigh your bird at least once weekly — twice weekly if you plan to place the bird on a restricted diet or a reducing diet to take weight off more rapidly.

You should not allow your bird to lose more than 4 percent of its body weight per week. Losses of 4 percent per week may be indicated for severely obese birds with accompanying health risks, but for mild to moderately obese birds a 2 percent loss per week is sufficient and also safer. You may be able to arrange weekly or biweekly weigh-ins with your avian veterinarian if you do not have access to an accurate scale. Scales with an accuracy of plus or minus 1 or 2 grams are acceptable, even for monitoring budgies.

Because pet birds are offered high-calorie treats and may not have the opportunity to exercise, they often become obese. Amazon parrots are particularly prone to gaining weight.

If your bird is on a seed diet, one of your first steps to combating obesity is to limit the amount of oil seeds, such as sunflower, peanuts or safflower, the bird has access to.

Encourage exercise by putting your bird in a larger cage than usual and placing its food and water as far apart as possible. Also allow your bird extra time out of its cage and encourage it to fly, climb or walk around under your supervision.

The first adjustment you should make in your bird's diet is to eliminate any high-calorie, high-fat treats, such as cheese, meat, fried foods, milk (bread soaked in milk), peanut butter and so on. You may choose to substitute healthier treats such as fruits, vegetables, plain pasta and unsugared cereals.

If your bird is on a seed diet, your next step is to either eliminate or limit the amount of oily seeds you feed your bird. Sunflower seeds, peanuts and safflower seeds are examples of oily seeds. They have high fat contents, which makes them quite palatable, but quite fattening as well. Buy a seed mix without these seeds and nuts, or pick out the oily seeds from your bird's current diet. Remove as many as you need to achieve the desired weekly weight loss. If your bird has been on a pelleted diet, switch to a brand with a lower calorie and fat content or reduce the quantity of pellets your bird eats by encouraging it to eat more fruits and vegetables.

RESTRICTING FOOD

If the increased exercise and diet adjustments outlined above have not been enough to achieve the desired weekly weight loss, the next step is to feed your bird a reducing diet or restrict your bird's access to food. Currently, there are a few commercially manufactured pellet and crumble diets for weight reduction (available through avian veterinarians), which are low in calories and low in fat. An alternative is to restrict your bird's access to food to two or three brief meals per day or to offer only a measured amount of food per day. Be sure to monitor your bird's weight and well-being when employing either of these methods. If

not done properly you may cause excessive weight loss and stress, which can lead to disease in your bird.

Most obese birds are normal birds that are inactive or that eat an improper diet. Be aware, however, that some birds may become obese because of hormonal treatments with testosterone or progesterone. Also, hypothyroid birds are prone to obesity. If your bird's obesity cannot be explained by inactivity or excessive caloric intake, thyroid function tests may be necessary. Consult your avian veterinarian.

Once your bird has reached its target body weight, begin adjusting its diet to achieve maintenance of that body weight over a month or more. If the bird was on food restriction, allow it more access to food. If it was on a reducing diet, switch to a relatively low-calorie maintenance pellet. In general, gradually increase your bird's caloric intake until your bird is no longer losing weight and is maintaining its desired body weight.

Just as with people, keeping your bird trim will contribute to its health and well-being. You will notice that your bird is more alert and active. It also will be less likely to develop fatty liver disease (a common pet bird malady associated with obesity), heart disease, lipomas, diabetes or egg binding.

Flap Those Wings

Mattie Sue Athan

Exercise is the expression of energy through activity, and few would disagree that a safely wing-clipped parrot has much physical and emotional energy to express. Some nervous energy can be expressed through normal exuberant vocalization, and both nervous and physical energy may be expressed in the process of avian bathing and preening after a thorough soaking. The energy used to recover from being completely wet at least a couple of times a week will prevent some frustration-related aggression.

Most important, ready access to both climbing and flapping exercise is necessary to ensure a long, healthy life and a good disposition for your companion parrot.

CONTROLLING OBESITY

It's not difficult for a pet parrot to become overweight within the first two years of its life. In fact, some owners might even believe it is desirable to encourage plumpness in a young bird. Newly weaned birds are typically a bit on the thin side, because they are just getting used to eating on their own, so many owners of such birds embark on conscientious programs to fatten up their baby birds.

Behavioral effects of keeping a baby bird plump might also seem desirable: minimal screaming, aggression and attention-demanding behavior during the developmental period. Within a few years, however, what probably amounts to a boredom-related eating disorder may blossom into lethargy, apathy, failure to talk, poor feather quality, feather-chewing, poorly functioning cardiovascular and respiratory systems, and a host of other disconcerting conditions.

Add the tendency of parrots to copy the behavior of their human companions, and we wind up with inactive, couch-potato birds that may become noisy and highly irritable if denied access to their favorite junk food. These captivity-related disorders are

Exercise in the form of wing flapping and playing with toys keeps a bird mentally and physically fit.

The coordination a bird develops from climbing on vertical and diagonal branches will help keep it healthy and agile.

may be almost invisible to anyone besides a knowledgeable avian veterinarian. The interference of fat with the functioning of air sacs can cause a bird to die from normal exertion—possibly leading to it literally falling from the air during attempted flight.

The initiation of an exercise program must be undertaken with special care if the bird is obviously overweight, exhibiting shortness of breath or is more than 10 years of age. A bird that has been relatively sedentary should be seen by an experienced avian veterinarian before beginning an exercise program, particularly if its food intake and weight have not been carefully monitored.

Many physical disorders in parrots may be related to poor cardiovascular condition. Improved circulation unquestionably provides benefits to eyesight and feather condition. Good circulation also helps to prevent wing, toe and foot problems, particularly in mature birds. Likewise, the sedentary parrot is in danger of suffering early symptoms of old age: impaired vision, failure to grow end primary feathers or poor-quality primary feathers, and circulation-related disorders in the feet and toes. Lack of muscle tone coupled with obesity is a common source of reproduction complications in hens — from infertile eggs to laying problems.

CLIMBING EXERCISE

Lack of a suitable cage in which to climb and lack of access to tree branches set in other-than-horizontal positions probably contribute greatly to broken tail feathers in young hand-fed birds. These birds fail to acquire necessary climbing experience, related muscle tone and coordination. I believe that horizontal perches are a factor in many lethargy-related disorders and that they contribute to gripping problems and fast-growing, needle-sharp toenails. I recommend challenging ropes and branches for optimum exercise. The coordination that develops

quite easily treatable and preventible.

Obesity in companion parrots must be addressed on two fronts: diet and exercise. While I am not qualified to discuss diet, I can speak with authority regarding the benefits of exercise.

PRE-EXERCISE PROGRAM VET CHECK

Although the behavioral effects of obesity may be readily observable to any student of parrot behavior, the physiological effects from climbing around on various vertically and diagonally situated branches will help keep a captive parrot emotionally as well as physically healthy and agile.

Owner participation in physical activity is highly prized by our human-bonded parrots. Macaws especially enjoy holding on with one foot while they are "slung" around like a daredevil child on a carnival ride.

A healthy, happy hookbill spends some time flapping every day, and many wing-trimmed companion birds prefer human assistance in making this possible. Be sure to monitor the bird's breathing. A sedentary parrot may be winded in less than 40 to 60 seconds of continuous flapping (a conservative estimate; some birds will require more flapping — sometimes much more flapping, as in the case of lories and small conures).

MODIFYING ATTENTION-DEMANDING BEHAVIORS

In addition to its use in the maintenance of good physical condition, required flapping exercise can sometimes be used in modifying screaming and biting behaviors. This is a manipulation of the stimulus/response scenario. Immediate and positive effects may be brought about by wobbling or quickly dropping the hand a biting bird is sitting on. The act of having to regain balance and the bird's sense that the bite (the stimulus) might have caused the "earthquake" (the response) can have powerful and immediate influence in modifying biting behavior.

Human-generated flapping exercises may also be effective in modifying some screaming and other attention-demanding behaviors. If the bird screams for attention when you leave the room, first try setting a good example for sound contact with the bird by calling quietly or by whistling back and forth. If the bird's screams continue, walk into the room (still continuing the

quiet "contact call"), ask the bird if it is all right (the bird might believe it is screaming out of great need). Give the "step up" command, then, with the bird holding to your hand, repeatedly move your hand down quickly and sensitively enough to induce the bird into flapping its wings for 20 to 40 seconds or until it is slightly winded. I call this the "P.E. Teacher" or "Drill Instructor" technique.

Required exercise is not a punishment (it contributes to the bird's well-being), although it may seem as such when administered by a determined, authoritative human. Once the bird learns that the stimulus (screaming for attention) brings a type of at-

A happy, healthy hookbill will learn to seek exercise merely for the satisfaction it provides.

Exercise in the form of climbing and flapping is necessary to ensure a companion parrot's long life and good disposition.

dency of our birds to self-mutilate with the use of daily flapping exercises. This activity stimulates the rate of metabolism and strengthens the cardiovascular system.

ENVIRONMENT, TOYS AND THE MOTIVATION TO EXERCISE

A physically and emotionally healthy companion parrot doesn't just sit around and wait for a friendly human to provide an opportunity for flapping. Many birds will grab hold of their cage bars and flap like crazy half a dozen times a day.

It may be necessary, however, to stimulate flapping exercise by providing toys. I find swinging toys particularly beneficial in this endeavor. I especially like interlocking rings — large enough to accommodate the parrot's entire body — hung vertically with a cowbell-style bell at the bottom. Metal rings can provide years of healthy climbing, swinging and flapping exercise.

A bird provided with a variety of toys will learn to exercise independently. Intermittent rewards of personal attention for self-generated activity will reinforce healthy patterns in the recently acquired companion parrot, but a happy, well-adjusted hookbill will learn to seek exercise merely for the satisfaction it provides.

tention it does not want, it will develop a more successful behavior, such as a quiet whistle or "contact call."

FLAPPING AND MODIFYING FEATHER-CHEWING BEHAVIOR

During the past year, I have seen dramatic results brought about by the use of exercise in the rehabilitation of feather chewers. Personally, I suspect a correlation between low thyroid/low blood pressure and self-mutilating stress reactions in hookbills.

Testing and thyroid supplements are important, but if there is no access to supplements, I believe we can lessen the ten-

Do Birds Get Colds?

Gregory A. Rich, D.V.M.

African greys are more susceptible to vitamin-A deficiency than some other parrot species. These parrots need diets rich in vitamin A to help them fight off upper-respiratory infections.

The term "cold" brings to mind sneezing, a runny nose, and sinus congestion and drainage. These clinical signs are merely symptoms of an underlying disease or condition, however. They do not constitute a diagnosis or a cause. Many causes of cold symptoms exist, not only in humans, dogs and cats, but also in avian species.

Two questions commonly asked by bird owners are: "Doctor, can my bird catch

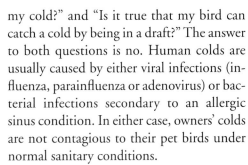

my cold?" and "Is it true that my bird can catch a cold by being in a draft?" The answer to both questions is no. Human colds are usually caused by either viral infections (influenza, parainfluenza or adenovirus) or bacterial infections secondary to an allergic sinus condition. In either case, owners' colds are not contagious to their pet birds under normal sanitary conditions.

It is a commonly held myth that a bird can catch a cold by being exposed to a cool draft. This is not true. Indeed, if any bird caught in a draft were to "catch a cold," then breeders could never breed parrots outdoors. I've seen countless pictures of Amazons, macaws, moustache parakeets, cockatoos and other psittacines perching at the uncovered portions of their flights with snow on the ground.

The more technical storyline about drafts and colds is multifaceted, but I will try to keep it simple. Drafts and air conditioning will not harm a healthy, well-adapted bird. On the flip side, a bird in poor nutritional condition, suffering from a viral, fungal or chlamydial infection (psittacosis), or intestinal parasitism, will have a compromised immune system that may be incapable of fighting off opportunistic bacteria ready to invade the respiratory system.

The stress of mating and rearing babies or stress from poor management and hygiene may also put a bird at risk. As is true with humans, bacterial organisms love a bird's upper-respiratory system. The environment in a bird's sinus (dark, humid and

Carrots are a good source of vitamin A, which helps prevent upper-respiratory infections in pet birds.

warm) is very similar to a laboratory environment in which bacteria are grown. In a healthy bird, the patient's immune system keeps the bacteria at bay. Add any one of the aforementioned disease states or environmental stresses, and the bacteria may flourish, while the patient's immune system is busy fighting other problems.

MALNUTRITION AS A CAUSE OF UPPER-RESPIRATORY PROBLEMS

Malnutrition has come to the forefront as a cause for many avian ailments. It has long been proven that seed-only diets, especially sunflower (white or black) and safflower,

without supplementation will lead to vitamin-A deficiency when fed for an extended period of time (more than three years). Scientists have also substantiated that certain species are more susceptible to vitamin-A deficiency: Amazons, Eclectus parrots and African greys. Birds require vitamin A to maintain the cellular bridges in the oral cavity and upper-respiratory system. These bridges keep bacteria, mucus and debris from gaining a foothold between cells in the oral cavity and upper-respiratory system. When the diet lacks vitamin A for extended periods, bacteria begin to gain entrance between cells and cause infection in the sinuses, oral cavity and windpipe (trachea). This infection results in sinus drainage, sneezing and signs of infection in the oral cavity.

Changing the diet or adding vitamins to the diet at this point will not cure such clinical symptoms. Competent veterinary care by an experienced avian veterinarian is needed to diagnose the condition and begin appropriate medical therapy.

Avian veterinarians accept as fact that a balanced diet for psittacines requires that a substantial percentage of food intake (30 to 50 percent) be from the fruit, vegetables and legumes categories. Canaries, finches, parakeets, softbills, touracos and other avian species have their own sets of nutritional requirements. It is best to obtain dietary information by asking an avian veterinarian or a curator of birds at a large zoological park, or from reading one of the many books about care of the species you are raising or are interested in. With proper diet, vitamin supplements and competent veterinary care, vitamin-deficiency problems can be prevented in any species. If symptoms surface, the problem can be addressed, treated and a proper diet formulated to prevent reoccurrence.

INFECTIOUS CAUSES

Infectious causes of cold-like symptoms in the upper-respiratory tract are quite numerous, yet they are easier to test for than vitamin deficiencies.

Sinus drainage and nasal discharge can be the direct result of bacterial infection by Gram-negative bacteria *(Pseudomonas, Klebsiella, Salmonella* or *E. coli)* or gram-positive bacteria *(Staphylococcus)*. Identification of the organism by bacterial culture is necessary to determine which type of bacteria is present and which antibiotic will be most effective in treating the condition.

Chlamydial infections (psittacosis) often show up as cold-like symptoms in larger psittacines. When a bird's immune system is compromised with psittacosis, it becomes easy for bacteria to invade the sinuses, an area with poor circulation and a prime environment for bacterial growth. It is imperative that birds with a sinus infection be tested for psittacosis. One often hears of birds undergoing treatment for "bacterial" sinus infections, only to have the patient suffer a relapse after the treatment is stopped. Many of these situations are due to primary conditions, such as psittacosis, that were neither tested for nor treated correctly.

Fungal organisms are another group of invaders of the respiratory tract that can be found by medical testing, such as cultures, Gram's stains or X-rays. The two most commonly identified organisms in this group are *Candida* (a budding yeast) and *Aspergillus* (a true fungus). These two organisms are also considered opportunistic due to the nature of their ability to cause disease. Quite often when one of these organisms is identified, a primary cause of poor nutrition, chronic conditions of poor sanitation or chronic stress can be determined. Treatment for either of these organisms also involves correcting the underlying conditions that initially led to the overgrowth of the organism. Treatment with antifungal medication must be under the advisement of a veterinarian, as these medications are prescription drugs.

Certain viral conditions may lead to upper-respiratory signs of illness. Amazon tracheitis, a herpesvirus, can cause such irritation in the trachea that a nasal discharge and a forceful cough may result. Secondary bacterial and fungal infections are quite common with this disease, so immediate attention by an avian veterinarian is advised.

ENVIRONMENTAL CAUSES

Chronic stressful situations, such as poor management (unclean water bowls, filthy nesting areas and poorly cleaned cage flooring), an incompatible cagemate or long-term inclement weather conditions are a few situations that could impair a bird's ability to fight off opportunistic infectious agents. Intestinal parasitism may also weaken a bird's immune system to a point where upper-respiratory infections are likely to follow. Avian mycobacterial infections (avian tuberculosis) have a similar effect on a bird's immune system.

A runny nose or chronic sinus infection in your bird may, and often will, be more complicated than it appears on the surface. Because life-threatening diseases, such as aspergillosis and psittacosis, can mimic any number of other conditions causing runny noses you should seek veterinary attention early in the disease process.

Also remember that if you have multi-ple birds in contact with one another, several may become contaminated with the same infectious agent; be sure to tell your veterinarian that other birds may be at risk.

Disease prevention will always be cheaper and more effective than putting out fires as they arise. So the next time your bird has a "cold," realize that more is required than administering some over-the-counter medication and hoping the symptoms will disappear. If they don't, the reason is probably that the underlying condition has not been properly addressed or treated. Keep your local avian vet's phone number handy. If you do not have one, a good starting point is to seek a veterinarian who is a member of the Association of Avian Veterinarians.

A balanced diet, including 30 to 50 percent fresh vegetables, fruits and legumes, can help a bird fight off upper-respiratory infections.

Common Illnesses

Douglas R. Mader, D.V.M., A.B.V.P., and Carl M. Palazzolo, D.V.M.

As a bird owner, you are responsible for providing proper care for your pet. The better educated you are about your bird's health, the better that care will be. An understanding of the more common illnesses that affect pet birds will allow you to communicate with your avian veterinarian more effectively should a problem arise.

Illness, or disease, can be divided into three general groups: infectious, metabolic/nutritional and environmental. An infectious disease occurs when an organism enters the body of a healthy individual and causes illness. Infectious diseases also have the potential to spread to other healthy individuals, thus causing disease in those birds as well. Examples of organisms that can cause infections include bacteria, viruses, fungi and parasites.

Metabolic/nutritional diseases are not caused by infectious organisms. Metabolic diseases are caused by internal disruptions in a bird's normal physiology, while nutritional diseases are induced changes brought about by improper husbandry. Metabolic diseases do not spread from bird to bird. Nutritional disease, however, is likely to affect all birds in a household if they are on the same diet.

The last group, the environmentally induced diseases, refers to all other causes of disease. Cat bites, broken blood feathers, fractured bones, poisonings and abnormal reactions to medications are just a few examples of environmentally induced diseases. Like the metabolic/nutritional diseases, these illnesses are not transmissible between birds.

INFECTIOUS DISEASES

Most bird owners are aware that bacteria can cause disease in birds. In avian medicine, bacteria are often termed as belonging to one of two different groups, called either the Gram-positive [G(+)] or the Gram-negative [G(-)] bacteria. The difference between these two groups is based on a test commonly used by avian veterinarians called the Gram's stain.

In avian medicine, the majority of the significant bacterial pathogens, or those bacteria that cause disease, are in the [G(-)] group. Common examples include *Pseudomonas, E. coli, Salmonella* and *Klebsiella.* Many different species and subspecies exist within each group. (An important note here is that although many [G(-)] bacteria cause disease, not all do and, as a result, not all [G(-)] bacteria need to be treated.)

A few bacteria do not fit well into any of the above groups. These are clinically important bacteria that, in some cases, not only cause serious disease in birds, but can also infect people. Examples of these unusual bacteria would include *Mycoplasma, Rickettsia* and *Chlamydia,* the latter being responsible for a disease called psittacosis. No specific symptoms are attributable to each of these bacteria. Rather, the symptoms are related to

Redness or swelling around the eyes can indicate upper-respiratory disease, a bacterial conjunctivitis or a manifestation of some serious internal disorder.

Any discharge or crusts around the mouth, nose or eyes should be considered abnormal. This is an example of scaly-face mites, a condition that is readily treatable when caught early.

the site of the infection.

For example, if there is a *Pseudomonas* infection in the lungs, the symptoms seen will be primarily respiratory. Sneezing, wheezing and rapid breathing may be obvious, but a lack of appetite, weight loss, feather fluffing and tail bobbing may also be noticed.

In general, most of the signs you see would be the same symptoms that are normally associated with any sick bird. Reddened, runny eyes with matted feathers around the nostrils can indicate ocular, nasal and sinus infections that are bacterial in origin. However, these same symptoms can also be caused by allergies, smoke irritation or any other type of upper-respiratory insult.

Bacterial infections of the gastrointestinal tract, such as collibacillosis, caused by *E. coli* bacteria, can show up as a lack of appetite, weight loss, vomiting and diarrhea. The feces may contain blood. Severe parasite infections can also cause similar signs.

Many viral diseases affect birds. Some of the more common viral infections include: psittacine beak and feather disease (PBFD), polyomavirus, psittacine proventricular dilatation syndrome (also called macaw wasting disease), Pacheco's disease and poxvirus. PBFD is caused by a highly infectious virus, called a circodnavirus, and is seen in many different species including, but

not limited to, cockatoos, African greys, Eclectus parrots, macaws, Amazons and Pionus parrots. A bird may be a latent carrier of the virus for weeks or even months without showing any signs of infection.

The length of time from infection to actual signs of disease depends on many factors, including the age, health status and species of the affected bird. Usually, the first clinical sign of a PBFD-affected bird is the appearance of abnormal feathers.

In younger birds, almost all feathers are affected around the same time, whereas in adult birds, generalized feather changes may take longer, happening over several molts. The beak may overgrow and develop cracks. The roof of the mouth can also become affected, which may make eating difficult for the sick bird. PBFD virus can be transmitted through a bird's feces, crop fluid, feather dust, and from an infected hen to her offspring through the egg. Some of these birds may die shortly after signs develop, and others may live for years.

Currently, no treatment is available for PBFD-positive birds, but an experimental vaccine is in the works. The best way to avoid PBFD-infected birds is to have your bird tested before purchasing it. The new PBFD tests will identify even birds that are not showing any signs of feather loss.

In the past, polyomavirus has been associated with budgerigar fledgling disease, but we now know it affects many larger psittacines as well. Although the virus is the same, the symptoms in budgerigars are different than those seen in other psittacines, where it usually occurs in young chicks. In young budgerigars, you may see abdominal distension and incoordination. Those birds that survive often have abnormal primary wing and tail feathers (referred to as French moult.)

In the larger psittacines, infected chicks may become depressed, lose their appetite, regurgitate, become afflicted with a delay in emptying the crop, and die within

24 to 48 hours. Often, however, no signs are noticed, and the chick is just found dead. Adult birds may also die of polyomavirus. Feather abnormalities are uncommon, however, and death may be rapid.

Transmission of polyomavirus is probably similar to that in PBFD, but this is not known for sure. There is no treatment for the disease, but a test is available to diagnose carrier birds that are actively shedding the virus. The test detects virus that is being released into the bird's feces. However, birds do not always shed the organism. For this reason, you should have your birds tested at least twice. An experimental vaccine is currently being studied.

Psittacine proventricular dilatation syndrome (PPDS), also known as macaw wasting disease, is suspected to be caused by a virus. This devastating disease affects psittacine birds and causes lethargy, incoordination, vomiting, weight loss, abdominal distension and passage of undigested seeds. Unfortunately, no known treatment exists for this disease, and affected birds can live several months to a year after the diagnosis has been made.

Pacheco's disease, caused by a herpesvirus, has been known to cause acute death with no warning signs, or it may cause typical sick-bird signs, such as lethargy, lack of appetite, vomiting, diarrhea (sometimes with discolored urates and/or blood), conjunctivitis, nasal discharge and, in some cases, wart-like skin masses.

Herpesviruses are highly contagious, especially in an aviary situation. Fortunately, if caught early, outbreaks can be controlled with a drug called Acyclovir. Also, a Pacheco's vaccine is available for birds in high-risk populations.

Poxvirus affects many species of birds, although the strains of the virus tend to be host specific. For instance, canary pox is different than falcon pox. Pox infections can manifest in three different forms: The first, which causes skin lesions in featherless areas,

is also known as dry pox. A wet form, called diphtheritic pox, causes respiratory disease. These first two forms can occur independently or together. They can also occur with a systemic form of the disease that causes depression, lack of appetite and death. No specific treatment for poxvirus infections is available, but some birds affected with poxvirus may survive the infection if treated symptomatically. Fortunately, a vaccine is available and is recommended for birds in susceptible environments.

FUNGAL DISEASES

Aspergillosis is one of many fungal diseases that can affect pet birds. It is seen in birds that have been severely stressed, malnourished or recently imported, and in birds that have been on chronic antibiotic therapy for some other problem. Antibiotics can depress a bird's normal microbial flora, thus allowing for an overgrowth of the *Aspergillus* fungus. *Aspergillus,* as with many fungi, is found everywhere in the environment. Some fungi are even considered part of the bird's normal microbial flora.

Symptoms of fungal diseases can vary, but usually relate to the organ system involved. For instance, an *Aspergillus* pneumonia will show up with respiratory signs. There may also be an associated depression, lack of appetite and the usual symptoms seen with any sick bird. With proper tests, most fungal infections can be diagnosed and, if caught early, effectively treated.

Many different parasites affect pet birds. These parasites can be either internal, as is the case with intestinal worms, or external, as in the case of mites and lice. One of the best examples of an external parasite is the scaly-face mite often seen in budgerigars. The mite, *knemidocoptes,* causes crusting of the beak and excessive keratinization of the scales on the legs. As with most parasites, this mite is easily diagnosed and treated. Response to treatment is best when the disorder is caught early.

Examples of internal parasites include tapeworms, roundworms and *Giardia*. Although you may occasionally see some of these parasites passed in your bird's stool, they are usually diagnosed by examining fecal material with a microscope. Symptoms can vary and may range from nothing in minor cases to depression, lack of appetite, vomiting, diarrhea, blood in the stool and weight loss in serious infections. Feather abnormalities can also be a manifestation of some internal parasites, as is the case in cockatiels with giardiasis.

METABOLIC/NUTRITIONAL DISEASES

Many diseases fall into this category. Examples of metabolic diseases include hypothyroidism (wherein a bird may be obese and show signs of feather abnormalities) and diabetes (wherein a bird may have a ravenous appetite, but continues to lose weight, is always thirsty, ingests large quantities of water and urinates profusely). The symptoms noted would depend on the disease present, many of which look similar.

Malnutrition is perhaps one of the more common problems seen in pet birds. Owners will often feed their birds very restricted diets, such as only sunflower seeds, merely because "It's the only thing that they will eat." People are afraid to try switching their pets over to a balanced diet because the birds may initially refuse to eat new foods. The owners become worried that their birds may starve, and thus restore the original, improper diet.

Signs of dietary deficiencies can be as simple as a poor feather coat or as severe as weak bones and retarded growth. Egg-laying hens on an improper diet may become egg-bound. Low-protein diets can affect a bird's immune system, thus making it more susceptible to infectious diseases. The symp-

toms of the infection might be the first abnormality noticed by the owner. Fortunately, in most cases, if the diet can be corrected and no permanent damage has been done, the pet will respond well.

ENVIRONMENTAL DISEASES

Symptoms of environmental diseases vary depending on the nature of the problem. A bird exposed to toxic fumes from burning nonstick cookware may simply be found dead, with no other clues as to the cause. A bird housed in an old cage that has been painted with lead-based paint may show all the signs of a severe gastrointestinal infection, such as weakness, lack of appetite and bloody stools.

Bleeding in a bird can be a life-threatening situation. Often, it is difficult to gauge exactly how much blood has been lost. It is possible for a small bird like a finch to bleed to death from a torn toenail. If you are not sure whether or not your bird has lost too much blood, take it to your avian veterinarian right away.

Illness can be triggered by many different causes. Perhaps the most important issue is not that there are numerous illnesses that can affect pet birds, but that many of the diseases we see have similar symptoms.

Because of these similarities, avian veterinarians may need to perform certain diagnostic tests to help differentiate these diseases. This is done for two reasons: First, diagnosing the disease correctly will lead to rapid and proper treatment for the specific problem. And second, once an illness has been diagnosed, your veterinarian can then give you a prognosis on how your bird will fare.

Early recognition of disease will increase a bird's chances of survival, regardless of the cause. Even if it is too late for the affected patient, rapid action may save other birds in the same household or aviary.

Preventing Nutritional Deficiencies

David J. Henzler, D.V.M.

Healthy birds spend a large portion of their day eating, drinking, playing and preening. This St. Vincent Amazon is enjoying some fresh red pepper.

In a survey conducted by the American Veterinary Medical Association a few years ago, avian veterinarians were asked to identify the illnesses they noted most frequently in their feathered patients. These vets indicated that 80 percent of the birds they examined for illness probably had a significant nutritional deficiency that contributed to their weakened conditions.

The introduction and popularization of pelleted feeds, changes in bird owners' attitudes concerning nutrition, and articles and books stressing proper diet and health care will eventually reduce the prevalence of nutrition-related bird illness. However, nutrition will remain a chief concern for bird owners for some time.

By nature, birds are gregarious. A survival technique they have acquired allows them to hide obvious signs of illness, because a bird showing overt signs of illness will be singled out and picked on by other flock members or pursued by predators. Birds have become masters of hiding disease symptoms, but by paying close attention to a bird's habits and physical condition, an informed owner can quickly become aware of potential problems.

GENERAL OBSERVATIONS

Healthy birds spend a large portion of their days eating, drinking, interacting with cagemates, playing with toys, nibbling on perches and cage wires, and preening feathers. (Note that some birds that inhabit arid environments in the wild — such as budgerigars — drink very little and are able to extract most dietary water from feed sources.) Many birds will sing, chirp, talk or make other sounds common to their species. The experienced bird owner or breeder is aware of these habits; with a little background and studied observations, the new bird owner also will gain sufficient knowledge to draw accurate conclusions regarding his or her birds' habits and health status.

Variations in any of the normal daily occurrences are reason for concern. Probably the greatest mistake bird owners make is failing to note such changes soon enough — when busy schedules reduce contact time with their pets.

Obvious signs of illness include: the bird sitting on the bottom of its cage, reduced interest in eating, failure to vocalize and fluffing of feathers. A bird exhibiting these signs is usually gravely ill, as it no longer has the strength to mask its illness. Therefore, bird owners should learn to recognize small changes well before their birds become seriously ill.

Both unusual weight loss or gain can be signs of malnutrition or other illnesses. In order to recognize a weight problem, every bird owner should first know the normal weight range for his or her bird. This can be done by weighing the bird on a fine scale at the veterinary office or by feeling the bird's breast on either side of its keel bone (the chest muscles in this area should gently slope and round out).

A prominent keel bone indicates that the bird is losing weight — the beginning of a malnutrition problem. Also, birds on seed-only diets may gain fat tissue beneath the skin. Excess fat can result in a fatty-liver condition and reduce liver function. Avian veterinarians will occasionally take blood from birds and run a packed cell volume (PCV). After the blood is spun down, an area in the tube sometimes forms that shows a fatty or lipemic serum. Often, budgerigars on fatty seed diets will have increased lipemic serum; this can be monitored, along with improving the bird's diet, as an aid in tracking its health.

SKIN AND FEATHERS

A bird's feathers and skin are frequently the most common areas in which signs of malnutrition can be observed. To understand abnormal changes in the integument, the bird owner must be able to recog-

Birds fed seed-only diets may suffer from feather and skin abnormalities, including extended molting periods, cracked beaks or dry skin.

nize normal skin and feather appearance. Generally, feathers should have a natural luster, be in the normal shades of color for the species and be tightly and smoothly fitted to the body contours. Newly emerging feathers in baby birds and in molting adult birds are protected by a plastic-looking feather sheath. Feather sheaths break down into dust as feathers mature.

Many birds, such as Amazon parrots, have fine hair-like feathers surrounding their nostrils. These structures are actually modified feathers. The lack of these or, particularly, the staining or wetting of these structures, can indicate a respiratory disease.

Vitamin A, which is either totally absent or present in reduced amounts in many seeds, is an important component in maintaining the health of the epithelial tissues lining the respiratory tract and in forming the skin of birds. Feathers are composed of 82 percent protein. Proteins are made of tiny building blocks called amino acids. Seeds lack some amino acids, such as lysine, methionine and cystine, and numerous vitamins. Therefore, birds fed exclusively seed diets are likely to have some level of protein deficiency.

When amino acids are lacking in the diet, feather and skin abnormalities can occur. These include: retention of pinfeathers or extended molting periods; crusted and cracked beaks; and dry, calloused skin and feet. Healthy birds on healthy diets have feet and leg skin that is smooth and free of dry, flaking scales. Malnourished and sick birds frequently have ruffled feathers. The immune systems of birds that eat unbalanced diets are weakened, and such birds occasionally manifest bacterial, fungal and parasitic skin infections.

LUNGS AND AIR SACS

In addition to lungs, birds have a complex series of air sacs, which are extensions of their respiratory system, continuing into the

head and wings. To function correctly, this system requires a balanced diet complete in vitamins necessary to maintain healthy epithelial tissues, which line the air-exchange surfaces.

Malnourished birds are prone to bacterial and viral pathogens. Signs associated with respiratory compromise include abnormal breathing patterns. Tail-bobbing and difficulty recovering from minimal exercise may also occur. A condition frequently seen in budgerigars is iodine deficiency or goiter. While this condition is not directly respiratory in nature, it can result in respiratory distress through the enlargement of the thyroid gland, which can occasionally put pressure on the nearby trachea.

More commonly, a physical mass or extension in the lower neck area is noted with occasional regurgitation. Treatment is generally successful. Swelling of the sinus and con-

A bird's feathers and skin are frequently the most common areas in which signs of malnutrition are exhibited. Feathers should have a natural luster.

A survival technique birds have acquired allows them to hide obvious signs of illness. A bird showing overt symptoms will be singled out and picked on by other flock members or pursued by predators.

junctival areas around the eyes can be associated with several pathogens, and, again, an unbalanced diet can contribute to these conditions. Occasionally, birds will sneeze. This is usually not pathologic, providing no discharge is associated with the sneeze.

GASTROINTESTINAL AND URINARY SYSTEMS

Perhaps the most sensitive indicators of avian health are the gastrointestinal and urinary systems. While they are essentially separate body systems, they share a common function — producing the bird's droppings. It is vital that the bird owner be skilled at interpreting the appearance of bird droppings. Changes in diet are manifested quickly in the nature of the droppings, as is a bird's health.

A bird dropping is composed of the feces from the intestine, and the urates and urine from the kidneys. Generally, the feces occupy the center of the dropping and usually vary in color from green to shades of brown. The urine usually encircles the fecal/urate margins and has a clear, watery appearance. A yellow or green color in the urates often indicates a metabolic breakdown of body tissues and is abnormal. An abnormal increase in urine (polyuria) can be an additional sign of metabolism of body tis-

sues. The urate portion is a type of solid urine and is mixed with or sits on top of the feces. The urates should be slightly off white. Birds losing significant amounts of weight will frequently manifest yellow pigments in the urates, which is a bad sign.

The bird owner can monitor changes in his or her bird's droppings by placing newspaper or similar material on the cage bottom and changing it daily.

When birds consume vegetables or fruits that contain a lot of water, a temporary increase in the urine portion of the droppings occurs. Should increased amounts or unusually colored urine persist, a nutritional, infectious or metabolic change may be the cause; this should be monitored and investigated by an avian veterinarian.

Gram staining of fresh feces is a common diagnostic technique used by avian veterinarians. Gram's stains differentiate bacteria into two groups: Gram-positive [G(+)] bacteria stain purple and usually represent normal bacteria, including lactobacillus; Gram-negative [G(-)] bacteria stain pink to red, usually showing undesirable bacteria. Birds normally have a combination of both, with the largest portion of bacteria staining Gram-positive [G(+)]. *Candida* organisms (yeast) are larger than bacteria and stain purple. A very common finding with birds on unbalanced diets is the absence of Gram-positive [G(+)] bacteria in the stool. Overall, these same birds frequently have scant amounts of bacteria, unless currently experiencing a bacterial intestinal infection.

In my experience, the lack of understanding of proper dietary needs of pet birds is the main reason birds suffer from all types of illness. Having a variety of food available for your bird is very important, as is utilizing quality pelleted foods; however, a strong knowledge and understanding of pet bird nutrition and proper diets are essential. The greatest investment a bird owner will make is improving the diet of his or her birds.

Psittacosis Update

Carl M. Palazzolo, D.V.M., and Douglas R. Mader, D.V.M., A.B.V.P.

Psittacosis (from the Latin word for "parrot"), is a very serious disease that affects both birds and humans. The disease is caused by an unusual bacteria called *Chlamydia psittaci*. It goes by a number of names in the pet trade and the bird world, often referred to as parrot fever, one-eyed cold ornithosis or chlamydiosis.

Although psittacosis is found in wild birds, it is more commonly detected in captive or pet birds. At least 130 avian species are thought to be susceptible, with 57 of these species in the parrot family. Many diverse strains of this bacteria exist and can infect a wide range of avian and mammalian hosts. One percent of the wild bird population is estimated to be either infected with or carrying the disease.

The Association of Avian Veterinarians estimates there are approximately 40 million pet birds. Estimates of the incidence of psittacosis range from 15 to 30 percent in psittacine birds, making this disease of great importance to all bird owners.

Legal precedents have been established in United States courts based on the ability of psittacosis to infect humans. This disease,

All newly acquired birds should see an avian veterinarian immediately after purchase. This initial vet visit should include a physical examination and diagnostic tests, including a test for psittacosis. Regardless of the results, quarantine new birds in your home for six weeks to prevent the chance of any disease spreading to your existing birds.

If a psittacosis-positive bird has been in your house, thoroughly disinfect a cage before introducing any new birds, and discard any wooden items in the cage.

instigated by stresses such as overcrowded cages, transport, changes in feed and recent importation. Psittacosis, therefore, is commonly associated with flea market birds, dirty pet shops and large, poorly managed aviaries. The *Chlamydia* organism weakens a bird's immune system, which results in the bird becoming susceptible to other bacterial and viral diseases. These secondary diseases can mask the symptoms of psittacosis, making a diagnosis even more difficult.

Symptoms of psittacosis vary tremendously and are influenced by factors such as husbandry, immune system status, virulence of a specific strain of *Chlamydia* and the presence of other pathogens (bacteria, viruses and fungi). Cockatiels and parrots tend to show a high degree of susceptibility. There are no specific signs that positively identify psittacosis.

In an all-too-common scenario, a pet bird will become ill three to four months after purchase. Most affected birds show a general "sick bird" appearance; that is, decreased appetite, lethargy, green diarrhea, weight loss, nose and eye discharge and sometimes, sudden death. These signs are common to many different bird diseases, and they don't necessarily mean a bird has psittacosis. On the other hand, many birds have this disease yet appear healthy. These birds are known as carriers, and they may eventually show signs of the disease, especially if stressed.

Establishing a positive diagnosis of psittacosis in a live bird can be difficult because no single test can diagnose the disease in all species. No test exists that can guarantee a bird is free of this disease. As in most diseases, a thorough medical evaluation involving history, physical examination, routine diagnostic tests, special tests and response to therapy are all necessary to arrive at a correct diagnosis.

Bacterial cultures are the preferred tests when seeking a confirmed diagnosis, since a

which has international implications concerning both humans and birds, is so important that the American Veterinary Medical Association held a symposium in 1988 on avian chlamydiosis. Some of the findings of these experts have been incorporated into this chapter.

THE DISEASE IN BIRDS

The disease is spread by inhaling dust from feathers and droppings infected with the *Chlamydia* organism. Transmission through the egg and parents feeding their chicks are both suspected as routes of transmission. Incubation time is highly variable, varying with the strain of *Chlamydia* and the species of bird. The disease is thought to be positive result cannot be disputed. Since birds with psittacosis can be intermittent shedders, owners or veterinarians must collect droppings over several days to help ensure a diagnostic sample. Upon submitting the sample, the organism can take several days to grow enough for detection and a positive diagnosis. This timetable can be too long for a severely ill bird.

Several tests have been developed to help overcome the disadvantage of the long duration required to both obtain a diagnostic sample and grow the *Chlamydia* organism in a culture.

The first, called an antigen test, evaluates a sample of a bird's feces for the presence of the *Chlamydia* bacteria. The test results are available immediately. Again, intermittent shedders can be major problems, because they can yield false negative results. Also, since false positives can occur when certain other bacteria are present, we advise using a second test for verification if the antigen test is positive.

The second test commonly used will also offer immediate results. This test requires taking a blood sample from a bird and sending it to a diagnostic laboratory where sophisticated tests determine if the bird has antibodies to *Chlamydia*. A positive test does not necessarily mean that the bird is currently shedding the organism and is infectious to other birds and people, but it does mean that the bird has at least faced exposure to the disease. A repeat antibody test two weeks later is sometimes necessary to determine if the infection is an active one. A disadvantage to this test is the fact that some results come back in the "gray zone," making interpretation and diagnosis difficult. Also, these tests may not be accurate in certain psittacine species, in young birds with immature immune systems or early in the course of the disease.

Other tests exist for diagnosing *Chlamydia* in live birds. Some of them are new and unproven, while others give results similar to the standard psittacosis tests. Psittacosis, however, is too often diagnosed through an autopsy.

TREATMENT

Psittacosis is a treatable disease in both birds and people, as long as there are no significant underlying problems and it is diagnosed in time. If a veterinarian suspects psittacosis, he or she is often wise to start treatment while laboratory tests are pending. All infected birds must be isolated from other birds and people. Many veterinarians recommend treating all birds in a household after one bird is diagnosed with psittacosis.

Tetracyclines are usually the drugs of choice for the treatment of psittacosis; the new generation of semisynthetic preparations are the most effective. They are useful only when the *Chlamydia* bacteria is actively replicating. Birdkeepers and veterinarians

Symptoms of psittacosis in birds include decreased appetite, lethargy, green diarrhea, weight loss, and nose and eye discharge.

Bacterial cultures are the preferred tests when seeking a confirmed diagnosis, since a positive result cannot be disputed.

ministration, are labor intensive and require accurate dosing.

Injections, while not approved for use in the United States, can be given once every five to seven days. This minimizes both stress and human contact and ensures that adequate amounts of antibiotic reach a bird's bloodstream. On the negative side, these antibiotics are expensive and are not readily available.

When treating birds infected with psittacosis, precautions are necessary to keep the circulation of feathers and dust to a minimum. Wet mopping with disinfectants is necessary. Persons who come in contact with birds receiving treatment should wear gloves and surgical masks when cleaning cages. The paper in the bottom of the cage must be changed frequently to prevent the build-up and drying of droppings. Cage papers, droppings and floor sweepings need to be put in biohazard bags for incineration or sterilization.

Treatment should continue for a minimum of 45 days, because *Chlamydia* can persist in cells without replicating, during which time they are not susceptible to tetracycline. This long duration of therapy can sometimes have adverse effects. Common problems are weight loss and secondary bacterial or fungal infections. The stress of capture or dietary change can be significant. If other diseases are present concurrently, a veterinarian may prescribe other medications. Birds do not develop immunity to psittacosis, and recovery from infection does not ensure lifelong protection. This is one of the reasons why a vaccine has not been developed for this disease.

All newly acquired birds should be seen by a qualified avian veterinarian immediately after purchase. This visit to the vet should include a physical examination and diagnostic tests, including a test for psittacosis. Regardless of the results, quarantine all new birds from any other birds in your household for at least six weeks to prevent any chance of any other diseases spreading

administer tetracycline in a number of ways, most commonly as a medicated feed, an oral preparation or an injection. The type of treatment utilized depends on the number of birds needing medication and the ability to capture and treat individual birds.

Flocks are usually treated with commercially purchased medicated feeds. Large birds are fed medicated pellets or medicated mash, and small birds receive medicated seeds. Some birds do not take well to the new medicated diet and never receive enough of the drug to eliminate the disease. Oral preparations require twice-daily adto your existing birds. If a psittacosis-positive bird has been in your house, thoroughly disinfect old cages before introducing any new birds. A diluted bleach solution (0.5 cup of bleach to 1 gallon of tap water) is sufficient to kill any remaining organisms. Discard any wood items in the cage, and replace them with metal or plastic. You can avoid potential problems by buying your birds from reputable dealers and breeders and avoiding places like flea markets and street vendors.

THE DISEASE IN HUMANS

Psittacosis was first diagnosed in humans in 1874. The actual organism that causes this disease was not identified until 1930. In 1929 and 1930, 1000 people were infected in 12 different countries (170 cases were in the United States) in an outbreak caused by the importation of psittacines from South America. The disease in humans occurs worldwide, the highest incidence being in developed countries where birds are kept as pets and where large poultry-processing operations occur.

Those at highest risk are people who come into contact with birds, even during such fleeting contact as construction workers exposed to pigeon droppings while they work. Inhalation of dried fecal dust or the discharges from nostrils or eyes are the usual modes of transmission to humans.

The incubation period is from one to two weeks. Certain groups are at a greater risk: children, senior citizens, people on medication and people with immunosuppressive diseases (such as AIDS). The usual symptoms in people are fever, malaise, headache and respiratory problems. Those who are around birds and have these or other symptoms should seek medical advice from their physicians. They should also let their physicians know that they have had contact with birds.

The latest information from the Centers for Disease Control states that there were 113 cases of human psittacosis in 1990. The average number of cases for the years 1981 through 1990 was 139 per year. From 1979 to 1988 only five people were reported to have died from psittacosis in the United States. Even though experts believe that human psittacosis cases are more widespread than reports indicate (probably due to the difficulty of precise diagnosis and the fact that people don't always tell their doctors that they face exposure to birds), the number of cases in relation to population is much lower than many other common diseases like leprosy, tuberculosis and malaria.

REGULATION

Regulations pertaining to psittacosis vary by state. In 47 states it is mandatory to report cases of psittacosis. Psittacosis is one of six zoonoses (diseases spread from animals to humans) that must be reported to health authorities. In California, an "Avian Psittacosis Case Report" is required from the submitting laboratory, the diagnosing veterinarian and the county health department. This is to ensure that the bird receives treatment and that its owners are aware of the potential public health problem.

The health department might investigate by visiting the location of the infected bird and identifying its original source. Depending on many different circumstances, the health department may quarantine the affected bird or aviary if necessary. Since pet shops are the major source of birds, a diagnosis of psittacosis in one of the stores can have serious economic consequences. Be aware that a lesser quality pet shop may not report such cases as a result.

In order to eliminate the threat to humans, the U.S. Department of Agriculture (USDA) banned the importation of psittacines in 1946. This ban remained in

If diagnosed early, psittacosis is a treatable disease in both birds and people.

purses. Confiscated birds were also put in quarantine, tested for Newcastle disease (which is a disease of particular concern to the poultry industry) and treated for psittacosis with medicated feed.

There is an inherent problem with this system. This feed is not always eaten in enough quantity to kill the *Chlamydia* organism. In addition to the inadequate amount of medication, the stress of capture, confinement and unusual food depresses a quarantine bird's immune system. These birds then enter the general pet trade.

Once these imported birds are in the hands of pet bird wholesalers and retailers, the problem does not diminish. Diagnostic methods currently available are inadequate for large-scale testing. Regulations are not easy to comply with and vary from state to state. Reliable information on how to control the problem is difficult for retailers to come by, and existing laws concerning this zoonotic disease are vague and out of date.

SUMMARY

Psittacosis is a difficult disease to diagnose, which hampers the identification of birds requiring treatment. The incidence of this disease could be reduced if more birds were treated prior to showing any symptoms. Unfortunately a safe and effective large-scale treatment program does not exist. The current importation and quarantine regimen does not ensure *Chlamydia*-free birds. An economical and effective means of testing and treatment is possible if a realistic approach is taken by all individuals involved in the pet bird industry.

Even though humans can and do get this disease, the rewards of pet bird ownership vastly outweigh the risks, especially when you compare the number of human cases of psittacosis with the tremendous number of birds in the United States that have the potential to infect humans.

place until 1967, when importation was partially resumed. In 1973, an outbreak of Velogenic Viserotropic Newcastle Disease occurred in the domestic poultry industry. This outbreak caused the USDA to require all commercially imported birds to undergo a 30-day quarantine period near the port of entry. During these 30 days, the birds receive treatment for psittacosis.

During the last decade, the United States imported more than 800,000 birds — about half of which were psittacines — from the wild. The birds went through quarantine in 80 USDA-approved, privately owned quarantine stations at designated ports of entry. During the same period, untold numbers of smuggled birds entered the United States through a variety of cruel and ingenious methods: in hubcaps, inside the panels of car doors, under car hoods and in

Avian Self-Mutilation

Terri Parrott, D.V.M.

Birds are complex creatures, and theories about their self mutilation are complicated as well. To simplify the possible origins of this behavior, I will divide self-mutilation into physical and psychological causes.

Physical etiologies include both infectious and noninfectious conditions. Infectious conditions may be parasitic (*Giardia,* microfilaria, mites), viral, bacterial or fungal. Noninfectious conditions include liver disease, thyroid hormone disturbance, adrenal gland disturbance, gonadal (sex hormone) disturbance, allergies or neoplasia (tumors).

The psychological factors of self-mutilation include such situations as the loss of a mate, the loss of an owner or someone the bird was close to, boredom, a new bird in the house, a new baby, strangers, a new job for the owner (with new hours and a change in the bird's routine), a new owner or a new habitat.

These are only a few of the more common situations that can disturb a bird's well-being. A careful history is one of the most important steps in evaluating a bird with self-mutilating tendencies.

MANIFESTATIONS OF SELF-MUTILATION

Self-mutilation may take many forms. The bird may pluck its feathers; it may only "shear" or tear part of the feather; or the bird may tear pieces of its skin off as well as feathers. Foot-chewing is also a form of self-mutilation — seen more commonly in Amazon parrots.

As exemplified by Amazon foot-chewing, many birds, by virtue of their species alone, may be predisposed to self-mutilation. The following species are commonly seen by avian veterinarians for self-mutilation: African greys, Amazon parrots, cockatiels, cockatoos, lovebirds, macaws (both mini and large species) and Quaker parakeets. Although these are the most often-represented groups, they are by no means the only species that exhibit self-mutilating behavior. Other species seen for self-mutilation, although in fewer numbers, are conures and some passerines.

Feather Plucking Frustration

Feather-plucking and self-mutilation are frustrating problems that occur for a variety of reasons. A bird that plucks out its feathers and/or tears off pieces of its skin (from its feet or body) could be suffering from any of a number of physical or psychological problems.

DIAGNOSING CAUSES OF AND TREATING SELF-MUTILATION

When you take your self-mutilating bird to your qualified avian veterinarian, he or she should run the following tests: weight, Gram's stain, complete blood count, serum profile (liver, kidney, thyroid), fecal (for parasite exam), gross and microscopic exam on feathers (if this is the problem), and cultures of lesions if needed. Other tests that may also be run include: a DNA probe for beak and feather virus (blood sample), a polyoma swab for detection of viral shedding, biopsies of skin and feather follicles, radiographs and endoscopy.

Once the bird begins self-mutilating, the inflammation that occurs causes more irritation and possibly secondary infection. This, of course, will cause the bird to bite and chew more. This cycle must be broken. While waiting for test results, many options are available to discourage the ongoing behavior.

Commonly available over-the-counter topical ointments offer limited success. You may also use bandages and collars with variable outcomes.

Drug therapy, using such anti-anxiety medications as Valium, is a common short-term remedy. None of these treatments are cures, though, and they certainly can add more stress to the bird, so talk

them over carefully with your veterinarian before implementing them.

Many of the physical problems that cause mutilation can be treated by medications, such as wormers for parasitic infections, or through diet changes for liver or kidney disease. Antibiotics are often helpful in fighting bacterial infections of the skin. Hormonal imbalances can be treated with hormone supplements, such as thyroxine.

Sexually related mutilation may be a bit more frustrating to treat. Oral and injectable hormone supplements must be used with caution because of side effects and risks of tumor formation. Sometimes the problem can be solved only after setting up the bird with a mate, and sometimes breeding birds that pick themselves also pick their mates and chicks.

Many birds' psychological problems can eventually be worked out by changing their environments. One owner found that he had to remove a piece of artwork he had recently hung in his living room before his cockatoo would stop plucking. If boredom or loneliness is the culprit, offer your bird new toys weekly and rotate them often. Playmates, such as compatibly sized birds, may also improve the situation. Again, use drug therapy only after all else has failed.

I believe I must add a word about nutrition and vitamins that birds need to remain healthy. No matter how varied your bird's diet is, an added nutritional supplement will enhance it. Vitamin E, selenium and vitamin A are all important for feather and skin health. Many good vitamin powders that you can sprinkle on your bird's food are now available. (Water-soluble supplements/medications tend to be unreliable due to intake variables in every bird.)

Remember that many cases of self mutilation can be successfully managed but may never be completely cured. A good history, a thorough exam by a qualified avian veterinarian and a healthy diet are important in evaluating these "problem children."

If your bird picks its feathers, as this yellow-crowned Amazon has, your avian veterinarian may recommend an Elizabethan collar to protect the bird's feathers and skin from further damage.

Avian Stress

Margaret A. Wissman, D.V.M., A.B.V.P., and Bill Parsons

You're finishing up your last day at work before you start your summer vacation, and you can't reach an important client who needs a report from you before you leave. The phone keeps ringing, and you have just realized you forgot to pick up your dry cleaning at lunch. Now the cleaners are closed. You're only half-packed and should have left work an hour ago. On top of it all, you can't remember if all your dive gear is in the dive bag. In fact, you can't even recall whether your friend Cindy returned your regulator.

The above scenario describes a stressful situation. Stress is an actual physical reaction to mental and physical tension or strain. Whether it occurs in a person or a bird, stress causes a particular series of events to unfold in a predictable pattern.

DIFFERENT STAGES OF STRESS

Stressors cause stress. Stress originates in the brain, and hormones send messages from the brain to other parts of the body. Stress can be broken down into three stages.

The first body response to a stressor occurs with an adrenalin rush and is called the "fight-or-flight response." This alarm reaction prepares a human or animal for immediate action. The feeling you get when you narrowly avoid a collision with another car or when a loud noise unexpectedly startles you is the fight-or-flight response. Your body prepares for action. It dumps sugar into the blood and diverts blood away from digestion, allowing for greater muscle tissue efficiency.

This is the type of stress a bird may feel when captured from the wild or when a cat knocks over its cage. At this time, the body releases cortisol — a steroid — into the bloodstream. This hormone suppresses the immune system and prevents swelling that may occur with an injury. Cortisol also reduces pain, allowing injured animals a chance to escape from predators.

The second stage of stress occurs if a stressor remains in the animal's environment. This second stage is the "stage of resistance." The adrenal glands, which produce cortisol, continue to supply the bloodstream and tissues with this hormone, and it continues to suppress the immune system. At this time, the animal remains physically prepared to deal with the stressor, and its internal system fights the effects of the stressor, often for long periods. As long as the stressor is present and the animal considers it a threat, the effects of stress remain in the system.

To prevent stress-related health problems, bird owners should provide happy, healthy, stimulating environments for their pets.

Provide a Peaceful Environment

To make your bird's life less stressful, provide it a peaceful environment with plenty of visual and tactile stimulation. A pleasant view out a window (not in direct sunlight) or in a nice room, colorful and/or chewable toys, interaction with its owner(s), and regular daytime and nighttime hours will keep your bird stress-free.

The third phase of stress is known as the "stage of exhaustion." During this stage, a bird is much more susceptible to disease from opportunistic organisms. Bacteria that are present in a bird's environment may make the bird sick because of its suppressed immune system. Viruses such as Pacheco's or polyoma may be activated and shed by the bird at this time. The cardiovascular and gastrointestinal systems may also show effects of chronic stress. The high cortisol levels may allow the growth of some tumor and cancer cells. Stress can also cause infertility and inhibit reproduction. Necropsies done on birds that have been sick for some time often reveal quite enlarged adrenal glands, showing the physical signs of chronic stress.

MENTAL STRESS

Stresses can be physical, mental or both. Although a stressor threatens a bird's internal stability, it does not necessarily pose an *actual* physical threat — a bird simply perceives it that way. A wild-caught bird that received rough treatment from a gloved hand will consider a glove a threat. Sometimes just the sight of a glove will send a bird into a panic. This glove is a fine example of a mental stressor. A child who repeatedly teases a bird, waving his hands around the cage, is another. Psychological stresses are very real and threatening to birds.

Other psychological stresses can result from a bird's physical environment. Strange sounds, new people or pets, changes in diet and moving to a new cage, room or house can all act as stressors. Abrupt changes in temperature or humidity can also strain a bird. People who keep their pet birds up until all hours of the night, disrupting normal sleep patterns, also create stress for their birds.

Separation anxiety is one stressor that warrants mention. People often ask us if it is more stressful to take pet birds on business trips and vacations than to leave them at home with a pet-sitter. That, of course, varies from bird to bird. Some birds freak out around cars, planes, hotel rooms and strange cages, but others mourn if separated from their beloved owners. One African grey patient of ours had an owner who traveled frequently to water-skiing tournaments. She left the bird at home with a roommate each time, and upon her return, she found the distraught little grey had plucked every feather he could reach. Birds that have bonded intensely to their owners probably suffer less stress when accompanying their owners on vacation, if hotels and travel parks allow them. Of course, if you do travel with your bird, make sure you have necessary health certificates, and check ahead to determine if your bird can legally enter the states you pass through. Quaker parakeets, for instance, are not allowed in certain states. If you are traveling out of the country, consult with your veterinarian about required tests and certificates for travel.

PET-SITTERS RECOMMENDED

To keep from stressing your bird, try to avoid boarding it in a stressful environment. By refusing outside boarding, you will decrease your bird's exposure to disease, and prevent the additional stress of having strange people and birds around. If possible, have a pet-sitter come into your home twice a day, to feed, water and socialize with your bird.

The last group of mental stressors includes overcrowded cages, unfamiliar behavior in other birds, and restraint and handling, especially while taming or training birds.

An example involves a lesser sulphur-crested cockatoo named Amelia. She is a very sweet, tame, talking bird who knows how to roller skate, ride a bike and do other tricks. When Amelia was put on consignment in a pet store that was not set up properly for boarding birds, she was transformed from her outgoing and fearless personality to a scared, shy and very quiet bird. She ran from people and stopped talking and doing tricks.

One day the store owner went to the bank and took her for a ride in the car. On the way, the bird babbled away and played, as happy as could be. Obviously, life in that store was a major stressor for her; she preferred to be an "only bird." If she had stayed in the store long enough, she would probably have become one very sick cockatoo.

Visual barriers between flight cages of certain types of birds — including African greys, Senegals and cockatoos — often help to increase production among the pairs. The barriers prevent antagonism and displaying between different pairs, reducing their stress so that they may breed. Some pairs of birds will spend all their time displaying and calling to others of the same species. Hawk-headed parrots, for this reason, usually need isolation from other pairs to achieve optimum production.

PHYSICAL STRESS

Physical stressors are very common in pet and aviary birds. Birds with subclinical bacterial or fungal infections have physical stress. These birds are fighting a battle within to keep their infections under control. Although they appear healthy, these birds are struggling to maintain homeostasis, or internal stability. They are not yet sick, but they also are not well. In an aviary, this is the type of bird we see frequently that won't breed. Once the physical stressors are gone, the birds usually reproduce successfully.

Another physiological stressor is nutritional deficiency. Birds that eat an all-seed diet suffer from malnutrition, as do fussy eaters that pick and choose only what they like to eat. Birds on poor diets often show "stress bars" on their feathers. These bars show up as horizontal black or transparent lines on the feathers. Perhaps these stress bars are most obvious on the long tail feathers of malnourished macaws. With improved diets and stable environments, these birds often feather into beautiful plumage.

Parasite infections are also physical stressors, and internal parasites, such as roundworms, also drain birds of essential nutrients. Tumors, which cause pain and obstruct normal bodily functions, are also physical stressors – as are toxins and poisons in the environment. Secondhand smoke from cigarettes and overpowering perfume odors also cause stress.

The regular routine of molting also stresses birds. During a molt, a bird is replacing old, worn-out feathers with new ones. This requires quite a bit of metabolic energy and extra nutrients to replace feathers.

Stressors may combine to have a cumulative effect. An imported, adult spectacled Amazon named Walker was purchased to sell in a pet store. Right out of quarantine, Walker carried the *Chlamydia* organism that causes psittacosis, and she had roundworms. Although the pet store initially quarantined her in the back room, she did not receive an immediate examination from an avian veterinarian.

The pet store trainer worked with Walker daily to calm her, but she was a nervous subject. Within a week of her arrival at the store, she developed a runny nose, started sneezing and passed bright green droppings. All her physical and mental stressors quickly broke down her immune system, and she developed a full-blown case of chlamydiosis (psittacosis). After a full examination by an avian vet, she received treatment for the worms and began appropriate therapy. When dealing with birds — imported birds especially — we must remember the various stressors in their lives. Virtually everything is new and frightening to them.

As we mentioned earlier, a stressor does not have to be an actual threat. Different species and individuals may perceive stressors differently, so what stresses one bird will not necessarily stress another. Also, what stresses a bird may not be obvious to the owner: There may be no recognizable signs.

MINIMIZING STRESS

We humans must deal with stress as part of our every day living. Likewise, birds must learn to deal with certain amounts of stress. As their caretakers, however, we must try to minimize this stress and provide our birds with the best care possible.

Proper care includes balanced nutrition, fresh water, clean cages, good veterinary care, and a consistent amount of attention and affection. A cage without toys and stimuli also causes stress. A cockatiel patient of ours has a great, stress-reducing view from a window overlooking the intercoastal waterway. Remember that a bored bird is a stressed bird.

Stress management works for people, and it can work for birds. Consider your birds' environment, and try to identify and eliminate the stressors you may find. For instance, did your pet start acting differently after you placed a colorful poster near its cage? Did a new, bright shade of fingernail polish alarm it?

Rats or mice scurrying around your aviary will stress your birds, and stress can cause infertility. When evaluating the stressors in your bird's life, consider its species, too. For example, African greys often don't like bright sunlight. If the sun shines in on your grey's cage throughout the afternoon, the bird might very well start feather-picking as a result of that stressor.

Make sure your bird is healthy. Take it to a qualified avian veterinarian at prescribed intervals for checkups. A healthy bird can deal with stress better than a sick one. Make sure your bird eats a nutritious diet, and supplement the diet with appropriate vitamins and minerals, as directed by your veterinarian. Vary the diet to ensure a broad range of nutrients. And if your bird does get sick from the stress of breeding, or from other stressors, take it to an avian veterinarian immediately for diagnosis and treatment.

Try to provide your bird with a happy, healthy environment, minimizing potentially dangerous stressors. Stress management for our birds is one way to help ensure that our pets remain healthy, and our aviary birds achieve wonderful reproductive success.

Emotional Health

Chris Davis

Birds need to be held and loved, but the physical interaction needs to be tempered by periods of solitary playtime on a playgym or in the bird's cage.

People have kept pet birds for thousands of years, yet, until recently, if you were to discuss your bird's emotional health with anyone but a few very close bird-loving friends, you probably would have been the object of concern or ridicule.

If most of your family and friends are not familiar with birds as companions, you may still be on the receiving end of a certain

amount of clucking and nervous looks by those who believe they are "only looking after your best interests." If this is the case, relax. You have finally been vindicated. Science is proving that your feathered friend is just as bright as you suspected — maybe even more so. Consequently, keeping your intelligent friend emotionally healthy is a critical concern.

If a bird's emotional needs are not met, a variety of behavior problems can result. Aggressive biting, screaming, feather picking and self mutilation are all behaviors that can be triggered by a number of situations; however, well-adjusted birds going through similar experiences will be less likely to seriously injure themselves or others. Like human children, they may behave obnoxiously for a day or two, but can easily be manipulated back onto the "straight and narrow" before much damage is done.

Some of the more frequently seen emotional problems that lead to undesirable behavior are simple, and others are extremely complex. Let's examine some common causes of emotional problems in birds and some hints for avoiding them.

OVERINDULGENCE

Contrary to popular belief, the majority of problems seen by a behaviorist are not caused by mistreament of the bird, but are a result of overindulgence by the owner. For example, although new bird owners are instructed that they should not hold their new feathered friends any longer than they intend to after the birds' initial introductory phase, many people do not understand the serious-

Food can be a source of interest and entertainment for birds. The corn on the cob in this peach-fronted conure's dish has captured its attention.

ness of the situation until it is too late.

Admittedly, most of us have met irresistible baby cockatoos; however, the act of constantly carting these birds about, clutched possessively against our chests, creates adult birds that have no other desire on earth but to be surgically grafted to their owners' bodies. Fortunately, science has not yet progressed to that phase; all that develops when the spoiled bird matures is an individual that screams or whines when left alone. Often, the behavior will be taken a step further, and the bird will decide that life with feathers is just too much to deal with. It will then proceed to denude various portions of its body.

Sharing life with a naked and screaming little maniac tends to disillusion the well meaning owner. Seeing a gorgeously feathered head (pluckers cannot reach their own head feathers) on a bumpy naked body often causes the owner to lose all pretense of patience and unconditional love, and, sadly,

owners in this situation frequently consider giving up their birds. This is made doubly unfortunate by the fact that the owner is frequently the direct source of the initial problem, and the bird often is passed from one home to another, a victim of its owner's misguided love.

Like babies of all species, birds need to be held and loved, but the physical interaction must be tempered by periods of solitary playtime in their cages or on a perch or playgym. They then learn to enjoy being members of the family, even when they are not being held by someone.

When the bird is playing by itself, the owner should reinforce this desirable behavior with verbal praise, a smile, a tickle or a favorite treat. At first a dangerous "Catch-22" phase may occur, wherein the bird will immediately exhibit some negative behavior as a result of the interaction. This is natural. Ignore it and walk away. The bird will eventually learn that it will be praised for being well behaved. Playing with the bird and a variety of toys is a healthy human/bird interaction and a wonderful substitute for the clinging parrot routine.

DOMINANCE

The emotionally healthy bird will have learned that it is not the dominant member of the household and will be content to fill the "child" role of the relationship. To bird owners who do a lot of reading about bird behavior, the repetitive use of the word "dominance" probably makes them want to run screaming down the street in frustration; however, there is a reason why it is written about so frequently. Because birds are, by nature, wild animals that do not see the humans in their lives as having any more merit than other members of their flock, the dominant bird naturally tries to control its human family (flock) members. This can eventually lead to screaming and aggressive activities, including lunging and biting.

In a flock situation, dominance is frequently exhibited by height; therefore, one of the ways dominance in a pet bird can be affected is by keeping the top of the bird's head at mid-chest level to the owner. This lulls the bird into feeling like a secure baby and often is sufficient in itself to temper feelings of dominance. This means initially keeping the bird off cage tops, high perches and shoulders.

After the bird's behavior has become more acceptable, liberties can be extended gradually, and most birds can be allowed to eventually play on higher surfaces. Be careful, though, to make it clear to the bird that the people are the parental figures before doing so.

BOREDOM

Humans are boring. In the wild, parrots always have plenty to do: gather food, chatter with friends, tear up seemingly endless miles of trees, care for young and dodge predators. A wild bird's work is never done.

In a domestic environment, people often forget that the average bird can become extremely bored if not given enough visual, mental and physical stimulation. Boredom often leads to adverse behaviors, such as screaming and feather-picking. Life should be interesting. A variety of toys, rotated on a regular basis, can be the source of many happy hours of activity for your bird. Some birds are frightened of new objects and

Offering a millet spray to a parrot is a good way to keep the bird entertained for hours.

will need to be introduced gradually to the idea of toys, but most of them enjoy playing with a variety of things, once they get the hang of it.

Food can be a source of interest and entertainment, as well as nutrition, and a varied assortment should be provided. I delight in seeing my parrots dive enthusiastically into their food bowls in the morning, trilling at the discovery of their favorite objects.

Corn on the cob; whole, raw green beans and peas in the pod; carrot wheels or sticks; green peppers with some of the core and seeds intact; whole, fresh chili peppers; and whole-grain breads studded with chunks of tasty and mysterious grains are only a few of the foods that your bird might find entertaining. Fussy eaters will need a slow introduction to new things (try cutting the food into small pieces), but should eventually enjoy them.

Television is appealing to birds as well as to humans. Children's programs are especially well received by the larger, rowdier parrots; however, avoid programs that show predators. Birds do notice what is on television, and can be frightened by things they perceive as dangerous. As with most of us, the financial reports will probably be boring to them, but the movement and talking can

help keep them company when you are away from home. The radio can be a source of entertainment, too, but be forewarned that birds seek to equal or exceed the level of noise in their environment. Choose your radio station accordingly — and carefully!

Birds are special companions. All too frequently, their purchase is an impulsive act, and little consideration is given to their needs and preferences. Emotionally, they function at the level of a 2- to 3-year-old child and will usually challenge their owners from that perspective, not out of malice, but merely out of a simple, childlike desire to have their own way, as well as to fulfill those wild animal needs they do not consciously realize they no longer require.

In addition to providing proper husbandry and affection, owners need to understand the unique emotional requirements of their avian companions and must gently and lovingly set guidelines for their healthy development. As with all situations precious to us, sufficient time spent in guidance and continuing maintenance can yield a lifetime of rewards. Most importantly, each bird needs to be acknowledged as an intelligent and integral part of the family unit, and needs to be loved and respected for what it is — not for what we want it to be.

Birds that are fussy eaters may need new foods cut into small pieces before they can accept them.

Signs of a Sick Bird

Bonnie Munro Doane

Detecting illness in a bird is much more difficult than doing so in a cat, dog or other mammal. Birds in the wild that exhibit signs of sickness will be forced out of the flock because they attract predators, so birds mask their symptoms until they can no longer do so. You, as your bird's owner, are its first line of defense against illness. You are the one most familiar with it and will notice the subtle changes in behavior and activity level that are often harbingers of disease, in addition to the more obvious indicators that tell you all is not well.

Although many people do not track their pet birds' weights, you should be aware of your bird's normal weight. Just as with baby birds, weight loss may be one of the first indications that something is amiss. It is also important to realize that sick birds usually manifest the same outward signs of illness, regardless of the cause. In other words, whether the bird has psittacosis, visceral gout or tuberculosis, it will appear ruffled, sleepy and depressed.

It takes the skill of a qualified avian veterinarian to diagnose the problem. The bird may have anything from an uncomplicated upper-respiratory condition that will respond rapidly to appropriate antibiotics, to aspergillosis, which is notoriously difficult to cure. Any indication of illness in the bird, therefore, requires medical attention. No sign of sickness is too inconsequential to ignore.

Obvious Signs of Illness

- Consistent change in appearance of droppings
- Decrease in level of activity
- Soiled or pasted vent
- Bleeding
- Feathers lost and not replaced
- New feathers with stunted or atypical appearance.
- Vomiting/regurgitation not associated with courtship
- Feathers ruffled consistently
- Sleepy appearance
- Cessation of talking or other vocalizations
- Droopy wings
- Decrease in appetite
- Horizontal position on perch
- Tail bobbing
- Sneezing
- Inability to remain on perch
- Runny or plugged nose
- Staining of feathers around nostrils
- Perching consistently with neck extended and beak grasping cage wire
- Bird on bottom of cage with obvious weakness

Subtle Signs of Illness

- Weight loss
- Swelling on bird's torso
- Decrease in preening and grooming behavior
- Sticky feathers on top of bird's head and on cage and its furnishings, due to regurgitated material
- Water consumption changes
- Frequent flicking of head
- Regression to infantile behavior in weaned or almost-weaned birds

Visiting an Avian Veterinarian

Pamela L. Higdon

Choosing an avian veterinarian may be one of the most important decisions you make as a bird owner. Each appointment, whether for a routine checkup or for a suspected illness, requires preparation if you and your bird are to get the most out of the visit.

If the visit to the vet is for a routine checkup, call at least a week ahead to make the appointment. Make a list that includes things you would like done. This might be an excellent time to have your bird's wings and nails clipped. List any questions you have about caring for your bird. These questions might include: how to bathe your bird properly, how to detect illness in your pet, which houseplants (take a list of names of the plants in your home) and foods are toxic to birds, which foods your bird needs for optimum health and your pet's housing requirements. Does your bird scream, bite or pluck out its feathers? Your vet will help you find solutions to those problems and many more.

If your bird seems ill, take a minute to write down your concerns and observations. As you write, try to decide whether you need an immediate appointment or if you can wait for a regular appointment. A list of problems might include: the appearance of the bird's droppings, the bird's activity level (is it more or less active than usual?), and its feather condition, appetite and beak condition. Has the bird eaten anything unusual? Each clue you provide will help you and the vet's staff decide on the urgency of your bird's condition.

Between the time you make the call and your arrival at the vet's office, add to your list of observations. Often, the stress and worry associated with an illness cause people to forget clues that could help the vet make a quick and accurate diagnosis.

PACKING FOR THE TRIP

Any time you leave the safety of your home with your bird, place it in a carrier, such as a travel cage or a pet kennel. Different birds require various types of containers.

I carry my cockatoo in a clear acrylic box equipped with a perch that was made

Before you take your bird to the avian veterinarian, make a list of questions you want to ask the doctor.

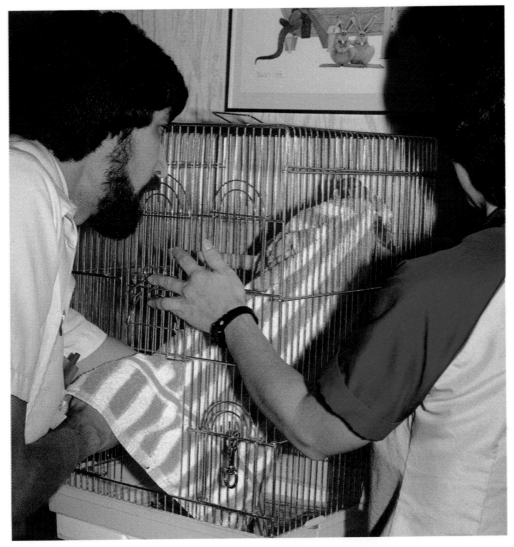

Once you are in the treatment room, allow the vet and his or her staff to make decisions about handling your bird. Give them any tips you believe might help aid the examination process.

just for him. He cannot chew his way out, but he can see what I am doing. Well-placed holes allow good air circulation. My wild caught, untamed Eclectus parrots travel in the car in a molded-plastic, portable pet kennel (the kind used for dogs and cats); this allows them to see and hear me, and they never try to chew the plastic. In addition, the two can travel in it together with plenty of room to spare. My smallest birds, parrotlets, easily fit into a small, hard-plastic pet box — the kind often sold to carry hamsters.

Whether you take your bird in a travel cage or a carrier, first remove all toys and other unnecessary clutter. Excess items in the

Items To Take to a Veterinarian's Office

- An uncluttered cage or carrier
- A clean towel or cloth
- Toenail clippers
- A list of plants you have in your home
- A list of foods you feed your bird
- A list of questions
- A list of observations that lead you to believe your bird is sick
- A list of things you would like done

Any time you leave the safety of your home with your bird, place it in a carrier, such as a travel cage or a pet kennel.

cage or carrier could injure your bird as you travel, and a lack of clutter will make it easier for you or your vet to remove the bird from the carrier for the examination.

I always pack a clean towel when I take my birds to the vet. I do so for several reasons: I can have the towel handy when the vet is ready to catch and hold my bird; I know the towel has not been inadvertently contaminated by another, perhaps infected, bird; and my birds are used to being caught and handled in certain towels. Similarly, I take along my own scissors or nail clippers when the vet will clip wings or nails.

THE TRIP TO THE VET'S OFFICE

Always secure your bird's carrier in the car with a seat belt. If you will travel for more than 15 minutes, place a plastic dish of fruits or vegetables in the carrier to help prevent your bird from dehydrating. If the sun is bright, cover your bird's cage to help prevent overheating. If the day is hot or cold, take adequate care to protect your bird from the stress of dramatic temperature changes.

As you drive, talk to your birds to reassure them. Play music in the car that your birds find soothing. This choice should be based on music they normally hear at home.

When you arrive at the vet's office, keep your bird in its carrier or cage in the waiting room. Your pet will probably be nervous and afraid. A large room full of other anxious pets will alarm your bird further if you remove it from the relative safety of its carrier. Also, if an infected bird is in the waiting room, you could expose your bird unnecessarily to airborne viruses and bacteria.

Veterinarians' offices are often filled with apprehensive or upset people and their pets. Be patient with the vet's staff as well as with other pet owners. As in doctors' offices, emergencies may take precedence over regular appointments, and you may need to wait longer than you had planned. When I am in such a situation, I remember the times when the vet has given me and my sick bird immediate attention, while others waited. I know how grateful I have been, and the thought helps me relax.

Once you are in the treatment room, allow the vet and his or her staff to make decisions about handling your bird. They may wish you to remove it from the carrier, or they may want to remove it themselves. Give them any tips you believe might help make the examination easier. Although most of my birds are easy to handle, for example, I always remind my vet that my two

Typical Questions From New Bird Owners

- What should healthy droppings look like?
- What foods should my bird eat? In what proportions? (For example, how many seeds in comparison to how many fruits and vegetables?)
- What is the best room temperature for this bird?
- How often should I bathe my bird?
- How should I bathe it? Misting bottle? Shower?
- How should I dry it?
- How often will my bird's wings need clipping?
- How often will my bird's toenails need clipping?
- What is a blood feather?
- What should I do if my bird breaks a blood feather?
- What should I do if my bird breaks a toenail and bleeds?
- Which plants on my list are poisonous to birds?
- Which foods are toxic to birds?
- Should I cover my bird's cage at night?

adult Eclectus parrots bite. She then handles these birds far differently than my tamer pets.

Because I want the staff to handle my birds only in the towels I have brought from home, I have the towels ready when they walk into the room. I also have my list of questions handy, with a pen or pencil to write down the answers. If I think my bird's droppings look odd, I have a sample or a detailed description.

Explain clearly and simply what you want the vet to do or look for during that visit. If you think the bird is ill, tell the doctor exactly why you came to that conclusion. If you are there for a regular checkup, ask what the vet will look for and what tests will need to be done. If you have additional procedures in mind, explain to the vet why you think they are necessary.

As the vet examines your bird, write down any important observations. As he or she tells you how to feed, handle, bathe or medicate your bird, write down the information. Reconfirm it by reading it back to the vet. This may save both of you phone calls later when you are unsure of your memory. As the vet works, reassure your bird by talking to it in a calm, quiet voice. When the visit is over, be sure to thank the vet and the clinic staff.

Later, as you drive home, talk to your bird to reassure it. When I bring my birds home from a visit with the vet, I offer them special treats, such as a fresh piece of broccoli that has been doused in water, a millet spray or a piece of cheese.

Whether for a wellness check or for a suspected illness, a visit to the vet can either be a stressful and upsetting experience or a reassuring and informative time. It's up to you. If you plan well, preparing yourself and your bird for the visit, you can make the trip the best possible. Your vet and the clinic staff will always be happy to see you, because you help them help you to the best of their abilities.

Poisonous Plants

The following common household items and plants are toxic to pet birds.

HARMFUL PLANTS			
NAME	**POISONOUS PART**	**NAME**	**POISONOUS PART**
Amaryllis	Bulbs	Henbane	Seeds
Azalea	Leaves	Holly	Berries
Balsam pear	Seeds, outer rind of fruit	Horse chestnut	nuts, twigs
		Hyacinth	Bulbs
Baneberry	Berries, roots	Hydrangea	Flower bud
Bird of paradise	Seeds	Indian turnip	All parts
Black locust	Bark, sprouts, foliage	Iris (blue flag)	Bulbs
Blue-green algae	Some forms toxic	Java bean	Uncooked bean
Boxwood	Leaves, stems	Jerusalem cherry	Berries
Buckthorn	Fruit, bark	Jimsonweed	Leaves, seeds
Buttercup	Sap, bulbs	Juniper	Needles, stems, berries
Calla lily	Leaves	Lantana	Immature berries
Caladium	Leaves	Larkspur	All parts
Castor bean	Beans, leaves	Laurel	All parts
Chalice vine	All parts	Lily of the valley	All parts (including the water in which they have been kept)
Cherry tree	Bark, twigs, leaves, pits		
Christmas candle	Sap		
Coral plant	Seeds	Lobelia	All parts
Daffodil	Bulbs	Locoweed	All parts
Daphne	Berries	Lords and ladies	All parts
Datura	Berries	Marijuana	Leaves
Deadly amanita	All parts	Mayapple	All parts, except fruit
Death camas	All parts	Mescal bean	Seeds
Delphinium	All parts	Mistletoe	Berries
Deiffenbachia	Leaves	Mock orange	Fruit
Eggplant	All parts but fruit	Monkshood	Leaves, roots
Elephant's ear	Leaves, stem	Morning glory	All parts
English ivy	Berries, leaves	Narcissus	Bulbs
False henbane	All parts	Nightshades	Berries, leaves
Foxglove	Leaves, seeds	Oak	Acorns, foliage
Golden chain	All parts, especially seeds	Oleander	Leaves, branches, nectar of blossoms
Hemlock, poison	All parts, especially roots and seeds	Philodendron	Leaves, stem
		Poison ivy	Sap
Hemlock, water	All parts, especially roots and seeds	Poison oak	Sap

HARMFUL PLANTS

NAME	POISONOUS PART	NAME	POISONOUS PART
Poinsettia	Leaves, flowers	Skunk cabbage	All parts
Pikeweed	Leaves, roots, immature berries	Snowdrop	All parts, especially buds
Potato	Eyes and new shoots	Snow on the mountain	All parts
Privet	All parts, including berries	Sweet pea	Seeds and fruit
Rhododendron	All parts	Tobacco	Leaves
Rhubarb	Leaves	Virginia creeper	Sap
Rosary peas	Seeds (illegally imported to make necklaces and rosary beads)	Wisteria	All parts
		Yam bean	Roots, immature pods
		Yew	Needles, seeds

SOURCES OF TOXIC FUMES

- Asbestos
- Bleach
- Carbon monoxide
- Chlorine
- Cigarette smoke
- Diazanon (DDT)
- Flea bombs
- Flea collars
- Floor polish
- Formaldehyde
- Hair dye
- Hair spray
- House paint
- Indelible felt-tip marker
- Kerosene
- Matches
- Mothballs
- Nail polish
- Nail polish remover
- Oil paint
- Oven cleaner
- Overheated nonstick cookware
- Paint remover
- Perfume
- Permanent wave solution
- Pesticides
- Shoe polish
- Spot remover
- Spray starch
- Suntan lotion
- Surgical acrylics
- Toilet bowl cleaners
- Wax

This is by no means a complete list. If you are unsure about the toxicity of any item, read the label.

Avian Anatomy

Robert Clipsham, D.V.M.

The natural beauty and variety of feathers provides the owner with an appreciation for the bird, and provides the bird with an array of important functions.

Modern avian anatomy is the result of nature's work through evolution. The bodies of some of the smaller dinosaurs were shaped into the perfect prototype to meet the requirements of flying, egg laying, rapid food processing and high-volume oxygen intake. Modern birds are the direct descendants of one of the two major groups of dinosaurs called Ornithischiais or "bird-hipped dinosaurs," and are the successors to a 228-million-year history.

Birds are simultaneously puzzling and fascinating when bird owners first begin to notice the anatomical differences between them and mammals. Despite the tendency to consider avian anatomy a dull and dusty subject, it may help you learn how to understand what makes your pet tick and how to help it in times of medical crisis, as well as to promote good health daily.

THE SPECIAL SENSES OF BIRDS

The special senses are a combined group of organs that allow all of us to analyze and define the world around us. These are the capabilities for sight, smell, taste and hearing.

Birds are reputed for their excellent vision. They are highly dependent on their eyes for food gathering, predator avoidance, breeding, nest-site selection and camouflage selection. Birds have especially well-developed optic lobes in the forward portion of the brain.

Avian eyes have tremendous variability in regard to their placement in the skull (forward with binocular vision for carnivores, and side vision for fruit-and-vegetation eaters); length of the eyeball (tubular for raptors and flattened for nonraptors to give them up to a 300-degree field of vision for spotting danger); and construction of the retina (the light receptor layer on the back of the eyeball).

Birds' eyes are huge compared to those of mammals. Birds' eyes average 1/30 of

A bird can raise its feathers individually by using tiny muscles attached to the feather shafts.

their body weight, in contrast to dogs, which have eyes that make up only 1/5000 to 1/8000 of their body mass. Despite this obvious advantage, the exaggerated claims of a bird's vision being 50 to 100 times more keen than that of a dog are untrue. Birds are estimated to have vision about two to four times as acute as that of the average dog.

The bird's range of vision is more limited than that of most mammals, as they do not possess the well-developed muscles for fine eye movement control, and the eyes are relatively fixed in the skull. Birds have adapted to overcome this serious disadvantage by having longer and more flexible necks that permit the head to rotate up to 180 degrees for an effortless rear view. Birds also have vision that is essentially two dimensional (hawks, eagles, owls and other raptors excepted). Most birds are forced to continuously cock their heads at different angles to build three-dimensional pictures by placing the objects of vision at multiple spots on the retina inside the eye. The brain compiles the multiple "snapshot views" to build a true picture of the object.

Birds can see in color, but the extent varies dramatically between species. Nocturnal species tend to have more rods in the retina (black-and-white light detection) than cones (color-detecting structures) to be able to see in dim light; the opposite is true for diurnal birds, in which color detection is critical for survival and reproduction.

THE SENSE OF HEARING

Ear function is rarely given any serious credit in birds, yet this is the reason that birds have developed their rich and complex sets of songs and vocalizations. The actual ear may be overlooked, since it lacks the fleshy sound wave-catching structure (what we consider the ear) of mammals.

If the tiny ear contour feathers behind the corner of the beak are parted, a small

The most obvious special sense for which birds are renowned is their excellent vision.

canal will be revealed. Hearing in most birds is extremely acute, and my wife tells me that many of my personal pets can distinguish my car engine from the other street noise before I pull into the driveway, even with all the windows in the house closed.

Hearing is actually the result of sound waves of compressed air striking the ear drum (tympanic membrane), which sets up a chain reaction of motion in the three tiny bones of the inner ear known individually as the hammer, anvil and stirrup. This bony chain vibration sets up a nerve impulse in the eighth cranial nerve, which is tied directly into the brain; what a bird (or anyone for that matter) "hears" is this electrical impulse registering deep in the brain centers.

The inner ear also has a major function in balance, which is critical for successful flight and steady perching. The vestibular apparatus is a tiny organ consisting of three fluid-filled tubes set at right angles to each other to monitor the position of the body as it sits in space. Fluid motion in one of the tubes will tell the brain whether the body is moving up or down, side to side or back and

forth so that the internal gyroscope, located in the cerebellum of the brain, can make the appropriate corrections when needed to prevent the bird from falling.

The sense of smell, with a few well-documented exceptions, is considered a limited, if not almost nonexistent, function of pet birds. The most famous exception is the kiwi, whose near state of blindness has forced it to develop an extremely keen nose.

Most birds, especially those commonly kept in captivity, are largely dependent on the visual aspects of shape, size, color and texture for food selection. Some new evidence suggests that perhaps smell is more important than previously thought but certainly does not influence daily activity as much as any of the other special senses.

One interesting species is Leach's storm petrel, whose delicate sense of smell can guide its navigation across the ocean and back to nesting sites on its seasonal migrations over extremely long distances.

THE SENSE OF TASTE

The sense of taste in birds has been explored only in a few species and would appear to be a rudimentary sense, according to medical statistics. Taste is the result of a chemical reaction at the taste buds, which generates a nerve impulse to the brain where a determination is made as to the degree of salt, sweet, sour or bitter that is present. Taste buds present on the tongue vary between species from a solitary taste bud in the Allen's hummingbird to 37 in a domestic pigeon to about 350 in the average parrot.

The average human tongue has approximately 9000 taste buds. Despite this obvious disparity, pet birds can be quite picky about their preferred flavors, and food often will be rejected by birds that have well-developed ideas of what is acceptable. It is impossible to say what part texture, temperature and size play in food acceptance, and no specific research has been defined at this time to sort those factors. Pelleted food manufacturers are investigating these specific issues to overcome what is a substantial block to complete acceptance of whole-nutrition diets — often the solution to birds suffering from severe "seed junkie" malnutrition problems.

AVIAN INTEGUMENT

The integument of any animal is defined as the structures covering the body. Most often this is considered to be the skin, or in the case of birds, the feather coat, since it is what the beholder sees most readily. In reality, the integument also includes the beak, claws, all surface tissues and the associated structures, such as feathers, oil glands and feather follicles.

Feathers are the most common reason for birdkeeping, in addition to birds' beautiful songs. The natural beauty and variety seen as different colors and plumage styles provides us with an appreciation for the bird, and provides the bird with an array of important physiological functions, such as flight, heat control, mate attraction, camouflage, water buoyancy (for waterfowl) and aerodynamic streamlining.

Feathers are actually modified scales evolved from birds' prehistoric ancestors and are outgrowths of the feather follicles of the skin. Collectively, feathers are considered to be skin appendages.

All feathers, regardless of color or shape, fall into one of three categories: 1) contour feathers, which are colored and visible to the eye; 2) down feathers, which lack the barbules to make them stiff like contour feathers – the resulting feathers are soft and flexible, enabling them to provide underlayer insulation; and 3) filoplumes, specially modified feathers, such as the "eyelashes" and "nostril hairs" seen on Amazon parrots and other birds.

Feathers are extremely rigid and strong structures. The contour feathers of the tail and wing edges are exceptionally long and are called "flight feathers." The reason that these feathers, which weigh only a few grams, can support a 2-pound macaw at 25 miles per hour is that the barbs that sprout from the main central shaft are locked together by even smaller barbules, much like a fabric hook-and-eye system. Every time a

Feather color is a complex combination of mixed pigments called carotenoids or lipochromes, which produce reds, oranges and yellows, plus melanin granules, which produce black, grays and browns.

Feathers are a science unto themselves, and most bird owners are amazed to learn that:

- feathers are arranged in well-defined lines running front to back down the body and are called pterylae or "feather forests"
- most birds have eight well-defined feather tracts, and essentially all feathers grow along or around them. Only a few primitive species grow feathers randomly
- feathers comprise 10 to 20 percent of the bird's body weight, depending on the species and climate or season
- birds in temperate or arctic zones have more feathers in winter than in the summer
- feather counts range from 1000 in some hummingbirds to more than 25,000 in swans
- birds maintain their body temperature of up to 112°F through feather insulation
- birds generally molt (lose their feathers) once to twice a year, and most species molt prior to breeding season
- feathers are dead structures, much like our hair, and are only fed blood during the growth phase when they are called "blood feathers." In this phase only, blood vessels provide nutrition for development
- feathers can be raised individually by tiny skin muscles attached to the feather shafts

bird preens its feathers, the beak is lining up and fastening this interlocking system together to keep the feathers ready for flight at a moment's notice.

Feather color is not just a colored pigment coated onto each feather. It is a complex combination of mixed feather colors called carotenoids or lipochromes, which produce reds, oranges and yellows, plus melanin granules, which produce black, grays and browns. In addition, turacoverdin produces a unique green pigment. The actual color perceived by the viewer's brain is the result of light absorption, reflection and diffraction, depending on the types and combination of pigments present. Remember that the white color you see in albinos is the absence of color altogether.

The remaining significant structures of the skin are the beak and claws. These appendages are really super-hardened layers of skin and are composed of a hornlike material called keratin. Keratin provides the wearers with a tough, renewable protective layer for chewing and climbing. This keratin layer protects the underlying vascular tissues, which nourish and renew them on a daily basis.

THE AVIAN SKELETON

Avian skeletons are rarely given any thought until an accident occurs that results in a broken bone. As evolution has reduced their density to allow for flight, bird bones are extremely lightweight and brittle in comparison to those of mammals. Certain ground-dwelling birds, such as the ratites (ostriches, emus and cassowaries) are exceptions to this rule; they are flightless, and their bones require the normal density to withstand the pounding that occurs in all animals that run.

Bird bones are microscopically and chemically similar to those of all other animals. Bones are living tissue with a high level of minerals, particularly calcium and phosphorus. Bone is an organic matrix composed of proteins with an organized mineral lattice for support and growth. Regular cell replacement is accomplished by constant nutrient intake via arterial blood flow. If bones were not living tissues in flux, broken bones could not grow back together, since the fracture line could never change and heal.

Contrary to popular conception, all bird bones are not hollow! Some of the heavier and nonweight-bearing portions of the skeleton have become air filled (also call pneumatized) to assist with flight; these include the upper wings (humerus), keel (sternum), pelvis (ileum and pubis), skull, wishbone (clavicle), shoulder (coracoid) and portions of the spine (vertebrae).

These air-filled bones are formed through extensions of the lung and air sac system entering the bone. It is critical to remember that a fracture of any of these hollow bones can expose a bird to potential infections of the respiratory system, as well as infections of the bones themselves. Therefore, steps should be taken to prevent the onset of respiratory diseases, such as pneumonia, air sacculitis and aspergillosis, if a fracture occurs in one of the pneumatized bones in which the damaged area is exposed to the open air or infection.

THE RESPIRATORY SYSTEM

The avian breathing system, and the highly modified organs that make this effort possible, is probably the single most unique aspect of bird anatomy – especially as compared to mammals. Because of the massive oxygen demand created by flight, traditional lungs are incapable of processing enough air in one breath to feed the muscles via fresh oxygenated blood in order to release the stored energy required for flying. Therefore, nature has taken the original bellows-type lung of the dinosaur and turned it into a free flowing, carburetor-type system.

The bird's respiratory system is typically divided into two sections. The upper tract includes the nostrils, sinuses, oral cavity (oropharynx) and windpipe (trachea). The lower tract in birds includes the wind-pipe split (bronchi), voicebox (syrinx), lungs and air sacs.

The air sacs are separate bag-like structures that sit in pairs on each side of the body and number a total of nine (four paired sacs and one single sac). The air sacs are extremely thin walled (approximately three cells thick) and allow air to be pulled through the lung and into the air sacs where it rests momentarily as an oxygen reservoir, while fresh oxygen is simultaneously pumped from the air sacs back through the lung for consumption in the same breath. The next air movement is to expel the spent air resting in the forward air sacs out the windpipe. This allows for continuous oxygen use on each breath instead of waiting to empty and refill the lungs each time, as mammals do. Birds actually breathe on a

Feather barbs that sprout from the main central shaft are locked together by even smaller barbules, much like a fabric hook-and-eye system. Every time a bird preens its feathers, the beak is lining up and fastening this interlocking system together to keep the feathers ready for flight at a moment's notice.

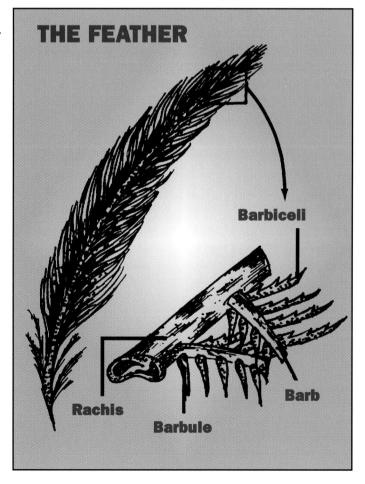

THE FEATHER

Barbiceli

Barb

Rachis

Barbule

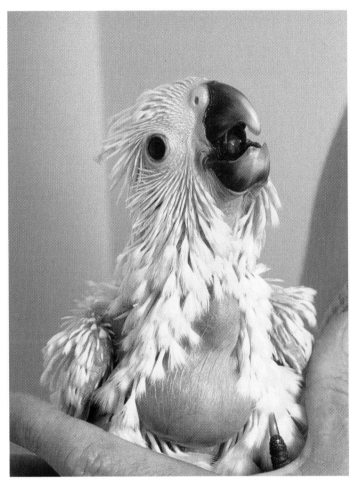

Much variation exists among bird species with regard to the size, location and stretchability of the crop because of differences in diet types, eating habits and body shapes. You can clearly see the bulging crop on this well-fed baby bird.

two-stroke cycle, and it is estimated that birds utilize oxygen approximately seven times more efficiently than mammals.

With all this improved function, birds have unique medical problems associated with the respiratory system. Because they lack a diaphragm and use the keelbone to mechanically pump air in and out of the lungs, pneumonia and other deep respiratory infections may go undetected for long periods of time. Fluids that would normally build up in the lungs and produce wheezing or coughing in a dog may settle into the lower areas of the air sacs and cause serious illness long before the bird shows any signs of distress. In addition, bird skeletons are rigid air frames that wrap around the internal organs, preventing easy access should any

surgery be required to correct a respiratory-system problem.

This is particularly evident when lung infections and air sacculitis problems allow mucus, fluid and infectious discharges to solidify into a rubbery mass. This is the case with chronic infection. Birds lack the enzyme coagulase, which helps turn infection (pus) into liquid in mammals so it can drain more easily from body cavities and other deep areas. Bird pus is like rubber and must be surgically removed.

This issue often becomes crucial when a pet bird with a chronic runny nose has masses in the lungs or abdomen at the time X rays are taken by the vet. The options that exist at this point are neither pleasant nor inexpensive. For this reason, avian veterinarians and seasoned breeders alike will state that "birds never get colds; they only get respiratory diseases" and "no runny nose should ever be allowed to run its course without proper medical attention." These axioms are repeated daily in bird hospitals to help save lives and educate owners as to this unique aspect of avian anatomy and physiology.

INTERNAL ORGANS

The internal organs are those vital tissue systems that process food for energy, move oxygen-laden blood to the body parts, continue the species through reproduction and process toxic waste byproducts for elimination.

The avian digestive system is not so totally different from ours, except that all birds lack teeth and are, therefore, dependent on the crop, which is a large holding bag in the lower part of the esophagus to store food; and the gizzard (ventriculus), an extremely muscular part of the stomach that is lined with a tough material — which, as a substitute for teeth — grinds up the bird's food.

Variation exists between bird species in regard to the size, location and elasticity of the crop (also termed the ingluvies) because of differences in diet types, eating habits and body shapes. For the vast majority of our pet birds, the crop is well developed and allows birds in the wild to swoop down to a food source, quickly swallow a large volume of food in sizable chunks, and fly back to safety in the treetops where the food can be regurgitated and chewed into more digestible portions at the birds' leisure.

The remainder of the digestive tract includes the first stomach portion, which is called the proventriculus. This section produces the acids and mucus necessary to start food digestion prior to entering the muscular ventriculus or gizzard. From there, the ingested food slurry exits the second stomach (gizzard) into the small intestine, and proceeds through the three successive sections of the small intestine — the duodenum, the ileum and the jejunum. Here, the true process of digestion occurs; bile from the liver and digestive juices from the pancreas are automatically pumped into the food as it passes to help break down the meal into its elemental components.

The small intestine wall is packed with microscopic fingers that create a huge surface area for absorption of fats, carbohydrates, proteins, minerals and vitamins. Once the food leaves the jejunum, it enters the large intestine, which in birds is very short and consists essentially of rectum (mammals have a very long colon as well). Here, water is absorbed from the used food as it prepares to enter the cloaca, or holding chamber, before it is passed out of the body as a dropping via the vent.

The average passage time for a typical parrot, mouth to vent, is about three hours and accounts for the 40 to 60 droppings produced each day by a healthy bird. The transit time and number of droppings can be affected by food types, such as fresh greens or fresh fruits; and various disease states, such as diarrhea, dehydration, hepatitis and infections.

The liver is the most obvious visceral organ seen during an autopsy or on an X ray, because it is relatively large compared to livers in mammals of the same size. The liver performs an amazing variety of functions, including protein metabolism, drug elimination, blood sugar production, bile manufacture, blood filtration and immune system assistance to name a few. The liver may perform 800 separate life-saving functions for its owner every day because of its intimate association with so many needs and its relatively large size. Bird livers are almost always affected by infections, and great care should be directed toward its support and care if a bird shows evidence of disease, toxicity or hepatitis.

The avian heart is anatomically very similar to the human heart. It has four chambers, is shaped roughly like a long tomato, and has the same basic input and output vessels as mammal hearts. The two top chambers are termed the right and left atria, and the lower chambers, which are more powerful, are called the right and left ventricles.

The function of the heart is to push blood through the lungs where carbon dioxide can be released from the body. It is exchanged for oxygen and carried through the arteries by the red blood cells.

Carbon dioxide picked up from the cells is pumped back to the heart and lungs via veins, to start the cycle all over again.

Here is a sample of different heart rates:

Species Heartbeats Per Minute (at Rest)

Hummingbird:	**500 to 1200**
Canary:	**795**
Quail:	**450**
Chicken:	**350**
Ostrich:	**175**
Human (adult):	**72**

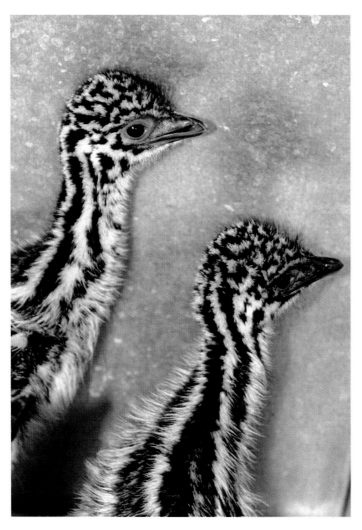

Certain ground-dwelling birds, such as the ratites (ostriches, emus, rheas and cassowaries) are flightless; therefore, their bones are of a normal density so they can withstand the pounding that occurs in all animals that run.

Heart rates can vary incredibly among bird species and, again, are dependent on size and flight requirements. Avian kidneys are slightly more primitive than those of humans and other mammals. Functionally, they are half mammalian and half reptilian. The goals are the same as for these other two animal groups: to eliminate the potentially toxic waste products of regular cell function, control water balance in the body, eliminate certain drugs and, unique to birds, shunt blood flow from the legs and lower portions of the body via a looplike venous system called the renal portal system.

This unusual two-way flow system is both beneficial and detrimental to birds. It can assist in blood-pressure control and shunt blood where needed in times of crises, but it also allows for infections that drain from the intestine (such as diarrhea) to have direct access to kidney tissues. The result is a potential kidney infection if intestinal disorders are not addressed in the proper medical fashion.

Anatomically, the avian kidney sits up inside two bony pockets in the pelvic bone; therefore, the major nerve (sciatic) and blood vessels to the legs pass directly through the kidneys instead of around them as in mammals. This point is particularly important when dealing with kidney infections, since one of the only significant visual signs may be a bird that sits low on its legs and acts like it is in pain. One- or two-legged lameness, or even paralysis, is a remarkably common occurrence in the budgerigar because of its susceptibility to kidney tumors (renal adeno-carcinoma).

Kidney tumors put increasing pressure on the sciatic nerve as the cancer enlarges within the kidney tissue, and its upward expansion is limited by the bony roof of the pelvis. No current therapy, either medical or surgical, has proven useful for this unfortunate condition.

The reproductive system of the cock is much more simplified than that of the hen. Its purpose is to provide viable sperm cells for fertilization of eggs. The components of the system include the two testes, the tube extending from the testes called the ductus deferens or sperm duct, and the attached cloaca where semen (the mixture of sperm and nutrient fluids) is loosely deposited over the vent of the hen.

A major difference between birds and mammals is that the testes are tucked inside the body cavity and held by connective tissue just in front of the kidneys. This is the reason that monomorphic birds require either genetic or surgical diagnosis to determine their sex. Birds are unique in this arrangement in that mammals must hold their testicles outside the body in a sac (scrotum) to keep them cool and prevent sperm death.

The reproductive tract of the hen is responsible for the creation, development, packaging and passage of the egg. This isolated life-support system is responsible for incubation away from the mother's body, and replaces the womb or uterus used during pregnancy by mammals. The entire time spent in the hen's body from ovulation to egg-laying is only about 24 hours — compared to slightly over two months in dogs for a full-term pregnancy.

The egg is initially stored in the ovary as a single cell containing only half the normal chromosome number of a regular body cell. The immature ovary may contain up to 10,000 ova in some species; however, only a very small number of these will ever be used (possibly up to several hundred) during the hen's lifetime.

The hen possesses only one functional ovary, which is present on the left side of the body and is attached at the same place on the kidney as the male's left testicle. The right ovary remains rudimentary (vestigial); however, in unusual circumstances, a right ovary may be present, or the right ovary will occasionally develop into an ovatesties if the left one is destroyed by disease or is somehow damaged.

In the immature hen, the ovary is tight, very uniform, flattened and slightly triangular in shape. As sexual maturity takes place, the individual ova start to enlarge, giving the ovary a more rounded shape. The ova are the egg cells and can vary from pinpoint to golf ball size in some species. Ovaries are pinkish-white to yellow in most species, but some birds, particularly the white cockatoos, will have black-pigmented ovaries.

Ovulation is triggered by a series of hormonal surges that is initiated by the release of hormones from the pituitary gland located at the base of the brain. Yolk is deposited in concentric layers around the ova to provide nutrition during incubation. The ova is released into the oviduct and enters the first section called the infundibulum. Fertilization occurs here if sperm have successfully made their way up the oviduct. The ova continues to migrate down the oviduct to the magnum where it receives several layers of albumen ("egg white").

The isthmus is the next section where the inner and outer shell membranes are laid down. The entire process so far has taken less than five hours. The membrane-coated egg now moves to rest in the uterus or shell gland where it waits for about 20 hours. During this time, the layers of calcium carbonate which make up the porous eggshell are secreted from specialized glands until the eggshell is thick enough to prevent trauma or dehydration to the developing chick once it is laid.

Once this is accomplished, the finished egg is quickly dropped into the vagina, wherein strong muscular contractions propel the hardened, moist, egg out of the cloaca and into the nest in only a few minutes' time.

CONCLUSION

This is only an overview of the avian body. The purpose of the information is not to intimidate or perplex, but to help you understand how a bird's anatomy works.

Practically speaking, by learning more about your bird's system, you will be able to recognize such medical emergencies as abnormal breathing symptoms, unusual droppings or a bird that appears to be eggbound. This short description of avian anatomy will certainly not make you a specialist, but it should assist you in making better decisions about what is normal or abnormal avian health, and it should make any future discussions with your avian veterinarian more productive for both you and your bird.

Managing the Molt

Elaine Radford

Red-factor canaries require color food during molting to maintain their coloring.

A bird may be unable to fly, whistle or build a nest, but if it's truly a bird, it always has feathers. In addition to giving flighted birds the power to take to the air, feathers may be color-coded to signal potential mates or to provide camouflage; fluffed out to frighten an enemy into thinking the bird is bigger than it really is; and puffed out or slicked down to main-

tain a comfortable body temperature. Because plumage is the most visible part of the bird, its condition signals health and beauty to mates, rivals and pet owners alike.

Most bird owners are already aware of the annual, semi-annual or ongoing process of the molt. Watching feathers drift around the bird cage like the aftermath of a pillow fight can be alarming, but every healthy bird molts, regularly shedding old feathers and replacing them with new ones that are growing in underneath. A young feather, often called a blood feather, is nourished by a blood supply through its shaft only while growing. Once the feather is mature, the blood supply dries up. Human hair that suffers from split ends continues to grow from the root, but a split, ragged feather cannot; hence the necessity of shedding the old to make way for the new.

REASONS FOR THE MOLT

Some birds undergo fascinating color changes as they molt. A young bird, inexperienced at escaping from predators, often has drab plumage to make it more difficult to see. As the bird matures and becomes more adept at escaping from enemies, it develops brighter plumage and begins advertising for a mate. Some species, like pin-tailed whydahs, may molt into their special breeding dress only during the mating season.

In species among which the sexes are visibly discernible (sexually dimorphic), the bird's first molt will divulge whether it is male (usually the more colorful of the pair) or a female.

Pearly cockatiels, a mutation developed by humans, are an exception to the rule that adult birds tend to develop flashier plumage than juveniles. A maturing male pearly will molt into normal gray plumage. Only the female retains her lovely coloring for life. The ideal breeder should warn the cockatiel buyer in advance to avoid giving puzzled beginners a shock.

A final reason for molting is to allow birds to sprout heavier plumage just for the cold winter months. As a consequence, a bird that molts into lighter plumage for the summer may temporarily appear to be losing more feathers than it replaces.

Feathers account for 15 to 20 percent of a bird's body weight, so it's little wonder that a heavy molt can make the bird room look like it has just received a fall of colorful snow. A canary or finch is the proud possessor of some 2000 feathers, while larger parrots have even more. At least bird owners don't have to sweep up after a whistling swan, which in heavy winter plumage boasts more than 25,000 feathers!

Commonly kept pet birds replace their feathers gradually, dropping a feather or two each day or so. When a feather falls from its follicle, the bird's body must work to replace it. The complete molt will, therefore, take place over an interval that depends on the season, the species, the condition and the age of the bird. Most molts begin with the flight feathers, continue to the body feathers and end with the tail feathers. The status of your bird's wing feathers will augur the full flurry of feather fallout.

ENERGY-DEVOURING PROCESS

Canaries and finches molt in sync with the seasonal light cycles of their natural habitats. Hardbills generally nest in spring, when

days are growing longer, so they will have more daylight to find food for growing babies. By the time the long days of high summer arrive, babies are out of the nest, and parents can concentrate on the demanding process of gathering food in order to replace their own worn feathers. For example, canaries normally molt in June, July and August, completing the process in September. Be aware that it's perfectly normal for canaries to cease singing during the molt, because they're conserving their energy for producing new plumage. The males will be singing again come fall.

Because of its natural response to light, a small bird could be inadvertently forced into a molt if exposed to too much artificial light. Any canary exposed to 15 or more hours of light a day may become stuck in a

Notice the unsheathed pinfeathers on the crest of this lovely cockatiel.

voted to their developing feathers. Others may become grouchy because of the apparent itchiness of the many young blood feathers. Mated parrots groom each other's pinfeathers in difficult-to-reach areas, but a single pet parrot may develop a spiky-looking head unless you teach it to accept the same service from you. I've found the molt is a good time to teach otherwise cautious parrots to enjoy being scratched on the cheek or crown, where they generally need help loosening the keratin (plastic-looking) coverings on new feathers. Just be gentle, and don't try to do too much at once. Eventually, you may be rewarded by a parrot that thrusts its head down and forward to ask you to pet its head.

Hookbills and hardbills alike generally enjoy plenty of baths or showers during the molt. Frequent bathing not only removes loosened keratin, which otherwise might look like dandruff, but it also seems to reduce some of that itchy, grungy feeling that comes with growing in the new feathers.

OFFERING THE RIGHT FOODS

Feathers are 88 percent protein, so birds must eat high-quality food to replace them. Canaries and many domesticated finches thrive on a high-quality commercial nestling food or a simple home-cooked egg food made from a hard-boiled egg mashed with one teaspoon brewer's yeast and a sprinkling of avian vitamin powder. Some finches, especially wild-caught African finches, may enjoy small mealworms or plump white waxworms. Special seed mixes containing small oily seeds like niger or flax will add a glow to a finch's feathers.

Parrots may enjoy protein-rich table food, such as well-cooked chicken or hardboiled egg. Pellets shouldn't be the entire diet, but they certainly have a place on the menu. Hookbills generally have, if anything,

Once your bird is finished with its molt, it will have regained full use of its previously clipped flight feathers. Make sure to reclip after all blood feathers are mature and the blood supply has dried up.

constant molt. Treat the problem by reducing the light to about eight hours a day for a week or so, then gradually work up to the normal amount of light that corresponds to the season. A cage cover will help finches and canaries get enough sleep and the right amount of light.

Many parrots are considered nonseasonal molters; these birds gradually replace their feathers year round. They don't necessarily molt at nice, neat, regular intervals like canaries. However, I can generally expect my hookbills to molt much more heavily during the hot summer months after spring breeding season ends.

A heavy molt can affect a parrot's personality. Some hookbills may become less talkative or playful while their energy is detoo much fat in their diets, so rarely would you have to increase the feeding of oily seeds like sunflower during a heavy molt.

Some birds, particularly red-factor canaries, need color food during the molt to look their best. Bird owners may choose between two forms of red-orange color pigment to enhance their pets' colors. Beta carotene is a natural orange pigment that gently intensifies color, and it successfully maintains the bright red color of a Pekin robin's breast. However, a red-factor canary won't develop its full color potential unless it receives a strong synthetic red pigment called canthaxanthin. You must separate red-factor and normal canaries during the color-feeding process when feeding canthaxanthin, because this pigment can turn the yellow birds orange even though they don't have the genes to become red.

To make sure that your canaries turn out evenly colored, give the same amount of pigment each day during the molt. Don't exceed the recommended dosage, because too much canthaxanthin can change a red-factor canary into an ugly, rust-colored bird that is stuck with your mistake until its next molt.

You can generally expect the new feathers to look shiny and bright. If the bird develops a bald spot or excessive numbers of ragged feathers that don't seem to get replaced, consult an avian veterinarian for advice.

Don't forget that a parrot's clipped wing feathers will be completely replaced by the end of the molt! Once the blood feathers mature and the blood supply dries up, clip them again to prevent an inexperienced or panicked flyer from injuring itself bumping into a wall or escaping through an open window. (Clipping a blood feather causes excessive bleeding and could result in death if the entire feather isn't plucked from the bird immediately.)

Molting can be stressful, but it's also perfectly natural. A little effort goes a long way toward keeping your bird's plumage glowing.

Many parrots are considered non-seasonal molters, which means that they gradually replace their feathers year round.

GLOSSARY

Air sacculitis: an infection of the air sacs; best treated aggressively with therapeutic agents that are chosen based on culture and sensitivity.

Amino acid: an amphoteric organic acid containing the amino group NH_2.

Antioxidant: a substance that opposes oxidation or inhibits reactions promoted by oxygen or peroxides.

Aspergillosis: a disease that is of economic importance to the poultry industry and is a frequent cause of respiratory disease in companion, aviary and free-ranging birds. Aspergillosis may be chronic and insidious, or it may cause acute death.

Aspergillus: any of a genus (*Aspergillus*) of ascomycetous fungi with branched radiate sporophores including many common molds.

Autopsy: a postmortem examination (See Necropsy).

Barb: any of the side branches of the shaft of a feather.

Barbule: a minute barb; one of the processes that fringe the barbs of a feather.

Candida: any of a genus (*Candida*) of parasitic imperfect fungi that resemble yeasts, produce small amounts of mycelium, and include the causative agent of thrush.

Candidiasis: infection with or disease caused by candida.

Canthaxanthin: a strong synthetic red pigment fed to yellow canaries to make them appear orange.

Carbohydrate: any of various neutral compounds of carbon, hydrogen and oxygen (as sugars, starches and celluloses) most of which are formed by green plants and which constitute a major class of animal foods.

Cardiovascular: of, relating to, or involving the heart and blood vessels.

Carotenoid: any of various yellow to red pigments (as carotenes) found widely in plants and animals and characterized chemically by a long aliphatic polyene chain composed of isoprene units.

Chlamydia: any of a genus (*Chlamydia*) of coccoid to spherical gram-negative intracellular rickettsial parasites.

Choanal slit: the slit in the hard palate of a bird's mouth that connects the nasal passages with the oral cavity.

Circodnavirus: a highly infectious virus that causes PBFD.

Cloaca: the lowermost portion of a bird's intestine, into which urine, feces, and eggs or semen are emptied.

Cuttlebone: the shell of cuttlefishes used for supplying cage birds with lime and salts.

Diagnosis: the art or act of identifying a disease from its signs and symptoms.

E. coli: bacteria that usually causes gastrointestinal problems.

Egg-binding: the occurrence of a hen having difficulty passing an egg; can result in death.

Endoscopy: the process of using an endoscope (a medical instrument) to view internal organs.

Etiology: the cause and origin of a disease.

Exotic Newcastle disease: a serious viral disease that poses potentially disastrous implications for the poultry industry. The threat of Newcastle disease has prompted the imposition of quarantine and bans in transportation of birds.

Gastrointestinal: of, relating to, affecting, or including both stomach and intestine.

Giardia: a flagellate protozoan; giardiasis is the disease caused by giardia.

Gram's stain: a method of differential staining of bacteria that is important in identifying bacteria.

Gram-negative: stain pink to red on a Gram's stain and are usually undesirable bacteria.

Gram-positive: stain purple on a Gram's stain and are usually normal bacteria.

Homeostasis: a relatively stable state of equilibrium or a tendency toward such a state between the different by interdependent elements or groups of elements of an organism or group.

Hookbill: usually referring to a member of the parrot family.

Hypervitaminosis: an abnormal state resulting from excessive intake of one or more vitamins.

Hypothyroidism: deficient activity of the thyroid gland.

Infectious: capable of causing infection.

Keelbone: the sharp bone that runs down between the breast area of a bird.

Klebsiella: any of a genus (*Klebsiella*) of plump, nonmotile, gram-negative, frequently encapsulated bacterial rods.

Knemidokoptes: infections so named after the mites that burrow into the skin and beaks of birds (especially budgerigars and passerines), often causing extreme deformity and/or loss of digits or feet.

Lesion: a sore.

Lipoma: a tumor of fatty tissue.

Malnutrition: faulty or inadequate nutrition.

Melanin: a dark brown or black animal or plant pigment.

Millet: a small seed often used in seed mixes; also fed naturally on dried sprays.

Mycoplasma: any of a genus (*Mycoplasma*) of minute pleomorphic gram-negative nonmotile microorganisms without cell walls that are intermediate in some respects between viruses and bacteria and are mostly parasitic usually in mammals.

Necropsy: a postmortem examination (See Autopsy).

Neonate: a newborn animal.

Obesity: a condition characterized by excessive body fat.

Pacheco's disease: disease virus associated with a systemic, in many instances acute, disease that affects the liver, spleen and kidneys.

Passerine: of or relating to the largest order (*Passeriformes*) of birds, which includes more than half of all living birds and consists chiefly of altricial songbirds of perching habits.

Pathogen: a disease-producing agent or microorganism.

Pellet: an extruded food product (diet).

Polyomavirus: a viral disease that can be passed from parent birds to young through regurgitation or from bird to bird via inhaled "feather dust" from infected birds.

Polyuria: an abnormal increase in urine.

Poxvirus: any of a group of relatively large, round, brick-shaped or ovoid animal viruses (as the causative agent of smallpox) that have a fluffy appearance caused by a covering of tubules and threads.

Prognosis: the prospect of recovery as anticipated from the usual course of disease or peculiarities of the case.

Proventriculus: the glandular or true stomach of a bird that is situated between the crop and gizzard.

Pseudomonas: Bacterial infection in which virulent strains can cause a septicemia that induces diarrhea, dehydration and dyspnea followed by acute death. Localized infections may occur in the upper-respiratory tract. Aviary outbreaks are common when organic material contaminates the water supply.

Psittacine: regarding parrots.

Psittacine beak and feather disease (PBFD): a chronic disease characterized by symmetric feather dystrophy and loss, development of beak deformities and eventual death.

Psittacine proventricular dilatation syndrome (PPDS): also known as "macaw wasting disease," disease marked by failure-to-thrive symptoms.

Psittacosis: an infectious disease of birds caused by a rickettsia (*Chlamydia psittaci*), marked by diarrhea and wasting, and transmissible to man in whom it usually occurs as an atypical pneumonia accompanied by high fever.

Quarantine: a state of enforced isolation.

Radiograph: an X-ray.

Regurgitate: the casting up of incompletely digested food (in birds, to feed young).

Rickettsia: any of a family of pleomorphic, rod-shaped, nonfilterable microorganisms that cause various diseases.

Salmonella: any of a genus (*Salmonella*) of aerobic, rod-shaped, usually motile bacteria that are pathogenic for man and other warm-blooded animals, and cause food poisoning, gastrointestinal inflammation or diseases of the genital tract.

Staphylococcus: any of various nonmotile gram-positive spherical bacteria that occur singly, in pairs or tetrads, or in irregular clusters and include parasites of skin and mucous membranes.

Tuberculosis: a highly variable communicable disease of man and some other vertebrates caused by the tubercle bacillus and characterized by toxic symptoms or allergic manifestations.

Urate: solid urine that is mixed with or sits on top of feces.

Ventriculus: gizzard

Zoonoses: diseases spread from animals to human.

ABOUT THE AUTHORS

Nancy R. Sondel has raised budgerigars for the past 12 years. She is an editor and columnist who composes a pet page for a newspaper in Soquel, California. She also is a freelance writer for McGraw-Hill Publishing Co. Sondel also provides a budgerigar phone consultation service for budgie owners called "The Well-Pampered Parakeet."

Pamela L. Higdon began keeping birds at 13 years of age, when she brought home a turquoise blue female budgerigar. She now lives with four parrots: an Eleanora cockatoo, a Vosmaeri Eclectus and a pair of Pacific parrotlets. Higdon is a former managing editor for *Birds USA* magazine and former associate editor for *Bird Talk* magazine; she is currently a contributing editor, writer and columnist for *Bird Talk*.

David J. Henzler, D.V.M., is the author of the book, *Healthy Diet Healthy Bird, Complete Guide to Avian Nutrition,* now in its third printing. He is past president and co-founder of the Maine State Caged Bird Society. He has written numerous articles on pet bird nutrition and bird health for *Bird Talk* and the former *American Cage Bird* magazines. He also developed the freeze-dried avian-specific *Lactobacillus acidophilus* product, Aviguard, by Pet Med Tech., Inc.

Dale R. Thompson, a dedicated aviculturist and wildlife photographer, worked at the Los Angeles Zoo for 10 years and was involved in some of the first successful toucan reproduction programs. He was also involved in four U.S. "first breedings" (giant tinamou, crimson-rumped toucanet, pale-mandibled aracari, New Guinea blood finch). He was the director of the Avicultural Institute for 11 years, a facility which contained approximately 1000 flights of 78 species of psittacines and nine species of softbills. His work has been published in numerous magazines and books.

Margaret A. Wissman, D.V.M., A.B.V.P., is a Diplomate of the American Board of Veterinary Practitioners, Avian Practice. In addition to six pet parrots, she owns an aviary of psittacines consisting of 50 pairs of parrots, several of which are endangered. She and her husband, **Bill Parsons,** own a breeding facility that is dedicated to the captive conservation of marmosets and tamarins, rock iguanas, tortoises and lemurs. Dr. Wissman keeps a large colony of green iguanas and is a contributing editor for *Reptiles* magazine, as well as *Bird Talk*.

Terri Parrott, D.V.M., works with the Florida Game Fresh Water Fish Commission, and treats injured and confiscated wildlife and birds for the South Florida area. She owns Pembroke Park Animal Hospital, a full-service rehabilitation facility in Pembroke Park, Florida. Author of the book, *Current Veterinary Therapy and Compendium on Exotic Animals,* Dr. Parrott is also a contributor to *Bird Talk* magazine and the American Veterinary Medical Association's *Journal of Veterinary Medicine*.

Denise Testa is current president of the Greater Rochester Hookbill Association. She has several parrots: an African grey, a green-winged macaw and a pair of Goldie's lorikeets. She also is involved in raising Siberian lynx and is a member of the International Society of Endangered Cats. Testa has written several articles for *Bird Talk* magazine.

Douglas R. Mader, M.S., D.V.M., A.B.V.P., is a veterinarian at Long Beach Animal Hospital, which caters to exotic pets. He has bred and raised African greys for several years. Author of the book, *Reptile Medicine and Surgery,* Dr. Mader also contributes regularly to *Reptiles, Bird Talk* and *Birds USA* magazines.

Gregory A. Rich, D.V.M., is owner of West Esplanade Veterinary Clinic and Bird Hospital in Metairie, Louisiana. His interest in birds began at 5 years of age, when he acquired his first bird: a budgerigar. When he was 10 years old, he and his brother raised approximately 100 quail. After completion of veterinary school, Dr. Rich acquired several parrots and now owns eight, including a breeding pair of hawk-headed parrots. Dr. Rich has been public relations chairman for the Association of Avian Veterinarians for the past five years and a former president of the Southeast Louisiana Veterinary Association.

Elaine Radford is a freelance writer and hobby breeder of peach-fronted conures and other small birds. She is the author of several books and has had numerous articles published in *Bird Talk* magazine and *American Cage Bird* magazine.

Jeanne Smith, D.V.M., is a veterinarian who specializes in avian medicine. She has operated an all-avian mobile practice since 1988, working with psittacines, ratites, poultry, canaries, finches, and racing and show pigeons. Dr. Smith has had numerous articles published in nine periodicals, including *Bird Talk, Bird Breeder, Parrot World, Exotic Bird Report* and *Avian Diseases.* She also contributed a chapter to the book, *Avian Medicine and Surgery.*

S. Blake Hawley, D.V.M., after several graduate courses in ornithology, was chosen for an expedition to the Outback of Australia to work with one of Australia's top ornithologists. He later attended the North Carolina State University College of Veterinary Medicine, focusing on avian and exotic animal medicine. Dr. Hawley has served on the board of directors for AERIES, a raptor and wildlife rehabilitation organization, and is an active member of the Association of Avian Pathologists and the Association of Avian Veterinarians. He is part of Kaytee Products' research program and serves as director of veterinary education and veterinary services manager for the Avian Research Center.

Randal N. Brue, Ph.D., has been involved in aviculture for more than 20 years. At one time in his youth, he personally maintained more than 500 birds. He has specialized in exotic bird nutrition since he graduated from Ohio State University with a Ph.D. in Nutritional Biochemistry. Dr. Brue has published several technical papers on poultry nutrition, avicultural nutrition and pet bird management.

Chris Davis, better known as "The Bird Lady," is an avian behavior consultant for pet owners, veterinarians and pet stores throughout the United States and Canada. Her career began in 1978 at Lion Country Safari, and she spent two years with the Universal Studios Animal Actors. It was during these years that she began to recognize the need for different taming, training and behavior modification methods than many of those being used at the time. Davis is a writer and lecturer on avian behavior modification for veterinary schools.

Mattie Sue Athan, who wrote the chapter on wing-flapping exercise, is an author, lecturer and consultant on companion parrot behavior. She has researched parrot behavior since 1978 and is the author of *Guide to a Well-Behaved Parrot* (Barron's).

Photo Credits: William Posnanski, Front Cover, 9, 16, 20, 46, 67, 68, 84; Bonnie Jay, cover inset, 56; Eric Ilasenko, Back Cover, 6, 8, 14, 22, 38, 40, 52, 60, 72, 91; B. Everett Webb, 18, 26, 32, 34, 35, 55, 70, 74, 79; Joan Balzarini, 19, 21, 23, 28, 31, 33, 37, 39, 41, 43, 44, 53, 54, 57, 63, 69, 78, 81, 86; Michael Defreitas, 36, 42, 51, 62, 88; Sherry Lee Harris, 25, 73, 80, 90; David Wrobel, 58; Douglas Mader, 47, 48; Norvia Behling, 13; Orv Beckman, 89.

INDEX